More Tales from Lark Rise

Betty Timms

More Tales from Lark Rise

*The childhood memories of
Flora Thompson's younger sister*

Betty Timms

THE WYCHWOOD PRESS

Our books may be ordered from bookshops or (post free) from
The Wychwood Press, Alder House, Market Street, Charlbury, OX7 3PH
01608 819117

e-mail: wychwood@joncarpenter.co.uk

First published in 2012 by
The Wychwood Press
an imprint of Jon Carpenter Publishing
Alder House, Market Street, Charlbury, Oxfordshire OX7 3PH

Second edition 2012

ISBN 978 1902279 47 3

Printed in England by CPI Antony Rowe

Contents

Foreword

We are indebted to Henry Westbury for his research into the life of Betty Timms and for editing and bringing into the public domain her fascinating novel. Like her better-known elder sister, Flora Thompson, she has drawn on the memories of her family and her childhood to write a fascinating parallel to *Lark Rise*, looking at the world of the 1890s rather than the 1880s. Betty has written about the same small north Oxfordshire villages of Juniper Hill, where the Timms family lived, and Cottisford where the children went to school, easily recognisable although not mentioned by name. The girls were the children of Albert Timms (renamed Robert in the book, as he was in *Lark Rise*), a stonemason who felt disappointed that he had not lived up to his full potential, and was not an easy man to live with. His wife Emma Dibber was the daughter of an agricultural labourer, who was also an eggler, selling eggs at the local market. Betty Timms reveals what a fascinating and strong character Emma was, reacting positively to the challenges facing her in life.

A potential solution to the mystery of why her brother Edwin joined the Yorkshire Regiment to fight in the Boer War is suggested by her writing about the group of young agricultural labourers who took a year's contract to work in Yorkshire where better wages were being offered; then, finding no pot of gold at the end of their rainbow, many of them emigrated to Canada or Australia. Edwin himself emigrated to Canada after leaving the army and Betty's younger brother, Frank, emigrated to Australia, as did Flora's own son Basil Thompson.

Few books on late Victorian country life have been written by the people who actually lived in poverty in the villages, as Betty Timms and Flora did, so they can both offer insights seldom found into how hard it could be. The middle class people who wrote about life in the countryside tended to give it a rosy glow not found here. Betty does not flinch from writing about the not infrequent deaths of babies and young children in the small community, and details some of the minutiae of the everyday life of the small world of her villages.

Betty and Flora were living on the cusp of change in the rural community, as more machines were introduced on the farm. The boys who would automatically have become farm labourers in an earlier world now found there were fewer jobs for them locally and some began new lives in the colonies, while others looked for work in the towns. The dreaded sanitary inspector was threatening to change their way of life by examining how unhygienic it was for them to have pig stys in their back gardens. Their isolated rural existence was gradually integrating with the outside world and women's roles were about to change.

Betty Timms has been much influenced by her elder sister, but she is writing from a slightly different perspective and her writing adds to our knowledge about village life, and she has new stories about some of the characters Flora introduced to the world, among them Queenie and the rector's daughter Grace. Her work is a charming complement to that of Flora.

Christine Bloxham

Acknowledgements

I must begin by thanking Christine Bloxham for kindly contributing the foreword and also for her friendly encouragement. Her book *The World of Flora Thompson Revisited* is a continual source of knowledge and is my inspiration.

Word processing from the 'working/reading copy' of the transcript presented a formidable task, especially when the text is interspersed with unfamiliar phonetic dialect, and I am therefore deeply indebted to my daughter-in-law, Alex Westbury, who eagerly accepted the challenge. I would also like to express my sincere gratitude to Jon Carpenter for his kindness in agreeing to publish the book, and for his patience, specialist guidance and encouragement.

Finally I would like to dedicate this book to my uncle and aunt, Leslie and Vera Castle, who both treasured and cared for Betty's wonderful typescripts to ensure that they could be enjoyed by future generations. Publication represents the culmination of their love for 'Auntie Betty' and her literary works.

Henry Westbury

Illustrations

Particularly for the benefit of those readers who may not be well acquainted with Juniper Hill and Cottisford, I have included a few illustrations to assist in setting the scene for Betty's novel. They are taken from some of my paintings which were produced following research involving old photographs and postcards, literary descriptions and other historical evidence. Betty, and indeed Flora, made no secret of the fact that their semi-autobiographical novels were based upon their childhood memories. The buildings they mention may have different names, but there is little doubt they are those which were familiar to them at the time and I have therefore attempted to paint them as Betty and Flora would have seen them.

Henry Westbury

List of illustrations by Henry Westbury

Introduction

Ethel Elizabeth Timms was born on 10th June 1886 at Juniper Hill, Cottisford and was baptised on 1st August 1886. Betty, as she was usually known, was ten years younger than her internationally acclaimed sister Flora Thompson.

At the tender age of 14 years, Betty began her working life as a domestic servant to the family of a Wesleyan minister in Brackley, but later she did follow in the footsteps of her older sister and became a postal employee. However, in 1918 Betty's postal career was cut short when she had to leave to care for her father, who had become very ill.

Following the death of their brother Edwin in 1916, Betty was the member of the family who most keenly shared Flora's interest in literature, and the desire to write strengthened further their very close and lasting relationship. Betty achieved success with writing competitions in 1924 and again in 1925, but in 1926 there was a major breakthrough when Harrap accepted her children's book, *The Little Grey Men of the Moor*, for publication. It is a delightful tale of two brothers who live in an isolated corner of Dartmoor. They are dwarfs who have special powers, and these enable them to converse with the four winds. The winds relate wonderful stories to the brothers, which are based upon their experiences gained as they traversed the globe. The book was well received and was clearly successful because it had a second printing in 1933. There is no doubt that Flora would have been very proud of her younger sister and the success would also have given her some encouragement with her own endeavours.

On the 17th July 1928 Betty, who was then 42 years old, married Henry Eastwood at Hungerford and they set up home together there. Tragically Henry died in 1930 at the age of 63, and Betty decided to move to Henstridge in Somerset.

Betty continued her writing with a 55,000 word semi-autobiographical novel entitled *A Pin to See a Pin-A-sight*, of which this book

Betty's nephew Leslie Castle with the typewriter that was used by Betty and Flora for their typescripts.

is the draft, an essay *Golden Wedding*, and a number of short stories, but it would appear that these were never developed beyond draft stage. Fortunately, however, the draft typescripts of these works did survive. Betty also wrote a further children's book entitled *The Island of Kaboo*, but again it would appear that this book was not developed beyond a draft stage. However, two draft typescript versions of the book have survived. The first shows on the cover 'by Elizabeth Eastwood, The Outlook, Dartmouth' and the other shows 'by Elizabeth Eastwood, Lauriston, Brixham'. These were of course two of Flora's addresses.

When Flora's son Peter was lost at sea in 1941, Betty helped her sister considerably by spending a great deal of time with her at Brixham. They both enjoyed browsing the local shops of books and antiques.

Betty was still residing at Henstridge in 1978 when Margaret Lane wrote to her concerning a proposed meeting, but shortly afterwards she was admitted to a nursing home at Devizes where she remained until her death in 1980.

Betty had designated her nephew, Leslie Castle, as her executor. His close relationship with Betty had been strengthened through grief following the death of Flora in 1947, and he had continued to visit Betty as often as he could until her death. Leslie had always shown a keen interest in the literary pursuits of Flora and Betty and he was therefore thrilled to find that he had inherited the typewriter that had been used by his aunts for their books, together with a number of other personal and Timms family items. He was however very surprised to discover the draft typescripts which Betty had written so many years earlier. Fortunately he treasured all of these items and eagerly added them to his private Timms family collection, which already included Timms family photographs and the numerous letters, which he had received from his Aunt Flora.

The typewriter made a brief appearance as the centrepiece of a display at the Lark Rise Festival, which was held at Shelswell Park in May 1976 to celebrate the Flora Thompson Centenary, and some access was permitted to Gillian Lindsay when she was researching Flora's biography, but generally Leslie felt strongly that his collection should remain in the locality.

I regarded myself as being extremely fortunate when my aunt decided to pass the collection to my safekeeping following the death of my Uncle Leslie. I spent some time in reflection and after discussion with my aunt, I decided to see if I could find a museum near to Cottisford where items from the collection, including the typewriter, could be placed on permanent display. Fortunately the Trustees at The Old Gaol in Buckingham welcomed the opportunity and subsequently 'The Home of Flora Thompson' exhibition was conceived and has continued to flourish.

Due to wartime shortages of quality paper, ink and typewriter ribbons, many of the words on the delicate typescripts are quite faint. These problems have been exacerbated by the passage of time and I quickly realised that urgent action was now essential to ensure Betty's fascinating stories and childhood recollections were not lost forever. Photocopies of the transcripts were carefully made and the faint wording was then overwritten on the copies in ink, to ensure that at least there were some 'working/reading copies' as back up.

As I began to read Betty's draft of *A Pin to See a Pin-A-Sight* for the first time, I soon became enthralled by the descriptions of people, places and events, the wonderful phonetic local dialect, which she used for the conversations, and also by her succinct social comment. I immediately felt an overwhelming desire to share this exhilarating experience with the many thousands who have previously been enchanted by Flora's *Lark Rise*. During their early lives at Juniper Hill, Flora and Betty did share the same environment and also some of their experiences, and therefore in some parts of the book there is an element of similarity in recollection. However, difference in age and personality has ensured that their viewpoints are generally quite different and therefore this book complements Flora's work beautifully. Schooldays, holidays, celebrations, working days, evenings in the public house and afternoons in the cottages are all described in detail, and Betty develops the lives of some very interesting individuals into wonderful cameos. Betty refers to herself as Eileen, and she refers to Flora and Edwin as Linda and Edward.

I should emphasise that Betty's typescript of *A Pin to See a Pin-A-Sight* shows a novel clearly at a very early stage of development, and as it stands it can only be described as a series of very loosely connected stories. Hence the title for this edition, *More Tales from Lark Rise*, was chosen to describe it with greater accuracy. It is also a first draft, and therefore I feel that any comparison with Flora's *Lark Rise* would be quite unfair. Flora was meticulous in her writing and in a letter to her nephew Leslie she explained her own particular process. She said that she wrote her books several times over, revising every paragraph and entirely remoulding many until she got them, not as good as she should like them to be, but the best it was in her to do. Flora's books also had the critical eyes of Oxford University Press passed over them before they were released. I was reluctant to make any significant alterations to Betty's work at this time, and therefore the text has been subjected to only minimal editing. When you peep into the wonderful pin-a-sight that Betty has created for us, I am sure you too will be spellbound.

Henry Westbury

More Tales from Lark Rise

'The End House' where the Timms family lived, as described by Flora in Lark Rise. Betty and her nephew Leslie Castle were born here.

High days, holidays and bonfire nights

The village was a sight for sore eyes – every cottage was bedizened with flowers, fairy lamps, gaily coloured pictures of the Queen in frames of red, white, and blue, golden crowns, flags, and bunting galore, while from apple trees and porches were suspended Japanese lanterns, and across the road were three triumphal arches – the old Queen herself might have been passing that way. Throughout there was a delightful air of expectancy.

From an early hour the schoolhouse, the focal point, for from here the grand procession was to start, had been a hive of activity. Long before the appointed hour children had been arriving from every quarter of the parish, little girls with wondering eyes, the ballooning skirts and sleeves of their freshly starched print frocks making them look like little boats in full sail. Little boys of all shapes and sizes, their hands itching for mischief, thrust into the pockets of sailor or knickerbocker suits, where they lovingly fondled the pennies they had wheedled out of mother or grannie for spending on sweets or swings, or rides on the wooden horses later in the day. All looked unnaturally good, and clean – at present.

They had all been up with the lark this morning to prepare for this wonderful day to which they had looked forward with longing for weeks past. A day, their teacher had told them, they were very privileged children to see, for never before had there been a Diamond Jubilee and in all probability there would never be another as long as England stood. It was a scattered parish and most of the children had a long way to walk before reaching the school house, and there were several minor accidents by the way – little Frankie, for instance, who with his two little sisters tarried to admire a litter of piglets in the cottage sty, over-balanced and fell in, to the ruination of his clean white sailor jacket and the little girls' frocks as they helped to rescue him. The trio howling loudly in unison returned home where their mother, who still had herself and two other children to get ready, was anything but pleased to see her offspring so soiled after all the trouble she had taken to send them forth spotless. So the day began with rather a clouded sky for that family.

Then little Elsie May tore all the gathers from the yoke of her best white frock while scrambling over a gate to avoid a cow, which some mischievous boys declared to be running amok just around the next bend in the road, and it would surely toss Elsie May like a pancake if she didn't run and hide herself out of its way. Although country children born and bred, they were terribly frightened of cows and would have bolted through a hole in the hedge that was scarcely large enough to admit a rabbit, to avoid meeting one face to face. They always said afterwards that they were bulls because it was supposed to be rather cowardly to be afraid of a mere cow, bulls were another matter, so they called them all bulls thus keeping their self respect.

Then Ann and Betsie, who live at an isolated cottage and had to cross the turnpike before they fell in with another group of children, peeping warily over the hedge before they ventured into that dangerous thoroughfare, spied someone and drew back in fear and trembling.

'A Turnpike Sailor!' whispered a frightened Betsie. Anne had never heard of a Turnpike Sailor, but knew it must be something terrible like Oliver Crumble or Jack the Ripper – names old Mark used to try to frighten them with when they lived near him and made too much noise at their play or threw their balls against the back of his house, they had no idea what these names signified but knew it was something awesome – like the big fire into which sinners were thrown. So the little girls turned tail and ran, and ran, and ran, making a wide detour over meadow, ditch and streamlet, until at long last they arrived at the schoolhouse, somewhat breathless and dishevelled.

When the Governess, who lived in a two-roomed cottage attached to the school, saw the children assembling she at first shooed them away steadfastly refusing to admit them until the proper time, so they played games and ran round and round the silver birch trees that canopied the school yard. She continued with her toilet – now and then she ran to the window and glanced up the road towards the vicarage – she too wore an expectant air, roses bloomed in her cheek and her pale eyes were bright, so that when she came out at last in her muslin dress and shady hat she looked quite lovely, which was strange because she was ordinarily rather plain.

'Come, children, don't run about so,' she called in an approach to her usual school marm voice – but the children could see through it at once and knew that they could do as they liked today as far as Governess was concerned and began to take advantage forthwith, as children will, some of them ran boldly into school to see what was going on, now that the door was open, others followed more shyly but all agog with curiosity.

From the classroom beyond came strains of music mixed with great shuffling of feet – as if the performers were restive and straining to be on the march. But No! Their instructor was adamant. All their repertoire must be gone through at this eleventh-hour practice to make quite sure of perfection. So the shrill sweetness of the flutes, the tap tap of the kettle drum, and the boom of the big one, added to the delightful ecstacy of the children.

Then everything else in the school was altogether different, the long desks with hard forms attached, on which they spent such bored and weary hours on ordinary days, were piled up against the far wall with the large crate which they had seen the carrier bring a few days ago. It was now empty for the beautiful china mugs that had travelled in it all the way from the Potteries now stood in rows dusted and shining on Governess's table. On either side of each mug was a picture of the Queen, her blue garter sash making a lovely splash of colour – here was the young Victoria in all the splendour of charming and slightly arrogant youth, and there the proud old Queen full of years and honour, her reign almost ended, the promise of her youth fulfilled.

The curate, who hadn't a shadow of the anaemic white guinea piggedness of the Victorian novels about him, had blown in like a west wind to see if he could help and now began to hand out the mugs one to each child as Governess called their names in the order of the school register although she had no need to refer to that document for she knew it by heart – not a very wonderful feat for from first to last there were no more than forty names.

Then the cardboard box that had been reclining in a deep drawer, the opening of which caused many a sinking of the stomach in times past, for it was where that dread instrument the cane was kept, but nothing so sinister came forth now. Out of the box came bright, almost silver, medals. When these had been given out the young clergyman, with clumsy hands, helped the smaller boys to pin them to coat lapels or sailor blouses where they looked splendid swinging from their red white and blue ribbons making the wearers feel like field marshals – at least. The little girls wore theirs suspended from pink or blue ribbons around their fat little necks. Little hot hands clutching their china mugs.

During the ensuing excitement there was a whispered conversation between governess and curate across the now empty medal box – two big girls standing near were all ears.

'What did I tell ee?' whispered Tessy Atwell to her companion 'Governess and Parson be sweethearts, that they be!'

'Ee called her Alice!' gasped Maggy Paxton in astonishment. 'It do seem funny, doon't it? I never thought of the Governess having a name like us afore, did you?'

In the meantime the band had emerged from the classroom looking very smart in Sunday suits with crimson shoulder sashes and peaked caps with insignia – this further glorified today with large rosettes of red white and blue – one worn on the left shoulder, another pinned rakishly to the right of the cap, the long ends all ablow giving a most 'devil may care' look. They were all boys in their teens – the young 'Gallants' of the village and its outposts, their rosy faces shining with soap and animation. 'Full on the devil they be,' the mothers were wont to say proudly when discussing them.

The bandmaster, however, had neither the honest blue eyes nor the taking ways of his pupils; his age was fortyish and he had a rather dissipated face and swaggering air. In black coat and vest and trousers of shepherd's plaid, he felt himself extremely dashing. A quantity of gold braid trimming his insignia declared his rank. He was not a native and people knew little about him, the only sure thing about him they said was his gift for music – in the opinion of some he could get a tune out of anything – even if it was only a small tooth comb. But then they were not over musical themselves and so easily pleased.

'Time we were moving off, Miss, don't you think,' he asked the schoolmistress in an affected voice, which always sounded so queer to the broad-spoken country folk and made them want to laugh.

Miss Day took the little silver watch from her belt and glanced at it unhurriedly – she was determined not to be flustered by Mr Moore or anyone else today. 'Well, perhaps it is,' she admitted after a moment's deliberation, and taking the 'Silence' bell from her desk rang furiously. 'Now children,' she cried as soon as she could make herself heard above the tumult. 'Line up outside and don't forget all I've told you. Behave well – especially in church, and you will have a very happy day which most of you will remember all your lives.'

At last they started off. The band struck up 'The Queen'. Mr Moore, wearing his hat at a nautical angle and swinging his Mallacca cane with great importance, took the lead. Then came the children arranged four abreast with the Governess and her two monitresses walking beside them at intervals to chide or encourage. The tiniest children riding in a flower-trimmed wagon brought up the rear, but as they went on their way up, down and round the village other people came out of their cottages, so that when they reached the church where the bells were ringing merrily nearly all the inhabitants of the village, the hamlet and outlying cottages were in the procession. The band played right manfully from the start to finish although their repertoire consisted of but half a dozen tunes – some of them not altogether suitable to the occasion, but all very cheerful and nice, adding much to the festive atmosphere. 'Rule Britannia' followed by 'The Queen', 'Auld Lang Syne', 'Annie Laurie', 'I'll hang my harp on a willow tree' and last but by no means least 'Ring the Bell Watchman'. This was a great favourite with both performers and audience so it recurred often out of its turn with the others. At the church gate, however, they gave up their music making to the bells – there were but two of them but they managed between them to make most joyful sound.

The little church was full to capacity. Eyes and hearts were over-flowing as those special hymns, which had been written for the ceremony and were at that very moment being sung in every church throughout the length and breadth of the land, were sung with great gusto and sincere feeling. What a volume of praise and thanksgiving rose to mingle with that of the celestial choir, for the blessings of sixty years' reign of Victoria the good. Sixty years of peace, and plenty – for some if not for all. Yet even here, in an obscure corner of her dominion, the good Queen's influence was perceived because from year to year they had felt a lightening of the yoke of poverty – even ten years ago things had been much worse that they were today. Now the bonny young girl of sixty years ago had become a frail old lady and they felt tenderly protective towards her – just as if she had been their own old mother or grannie.

All pathos slipped away as they filed out of the church into the golden sunshine of the lovely June day. Smiles, nods and hearty greet-ings from this one and that one. All were on the best of terms. The richest man in the neighbourhood shaking hands and joking with poor old men of parish pay, like old George Sairn who was almost double with rheumatism and a life of hard toil in general. With great munificence the Squire bequeathed a shilling to each on George and his cronies bidding them to spend it on coconut shys, switchbacks, or swings, just as they'd a mind, but not to make themselves tipsy with it whatever else they did!

'Thank ee, sir,' said George. 'Now I'll be bound, sir, you doon't remember coronation on our Queen. You udn't be born then maybe. But yure father, old Squire, ee wus there and se'ed me win the victory in that there race for bwoys over ten years old – an I be a gooing to win it today or I'll et me Sunday breeches, so mark me word that I ull.'

The Squire laughed heartily as he joined his own select little party of ladies. His mother, who had been a girl when Victoria ascended the throne and like other girls of that period had modelled her dress and demeanour on that of the young Queen, had in sixty years' constancy to that illustrious lady become exactly like her – in fact she out queened the Queen in her proud and haughty manner. She looked from a tremendous height on the working people and was greatly

Cottisford Church. The tiny church where the Timms family worshipped.

concerned at that time that they were getting above themselves, it was rare now for a woman or girl to drop her a curtsy. What ever was the world coming to!? Her daughters were a little more unbending but they too were elegant and remote, they smiled wanly on the lower orders because they wished to be friendly, for they must keep pace with the world and the world was changing daily – it was all very difficult for them. Their own young daughters did not find it so hard to smile back almost genially at the village girls.

The feast was spread in a large barn at a nearby farm and thitherwards streamed the merrymakers. The gaiety of the scene was breathtaking. Union Jacks dangled from every rafter of the roof and the walls were completely concealed by banks of flowers and evergreens; long trestle tables covered in snowy cloth and adorned with pots of cottage garden and wild flowers, collected by the schoolchildren before the dew was off them, filled the length and breadth of the barn. While everybody found themselves seats at the table the food was brought in hot and piping from the farmhouse kitchen, where a dozen women had been in their glory all the morning. Now they came forth, hot and flustered – but victorious, bearing gigantic dishes the likes of which will never more be seen unless as plaques upon parlour walls or for other such arty uses; these contained luscious sirloins of beef and enormous Yorkshire puddings. They were placed at intervals down the tables and before each stood a beaming farmer with carving knife and fork poised ready for action. Every one of the pile of large plates (and they were large indeed, like those one comes across that have belonged to old dinner services and not the scraggy little things one buys today to eat one's meagre rations from) was covered with juicy beef so that not a vestige of the china was visible, and an immense square of pudding was placed on top; by then the women had come back laden with dishes of cauliflower and floury white potatoes which they ladled out lavishly onto the already full plates, and they were passed down the table amidst a chorus of appreciative murmurs.

There was a 'High table' provided for the 'Betters' in a secluded corner of the barn. They did not sit down to it at present, however, but looked on in amazed amusement at the rapidity with which the plates were cleared and handed back to the carver for replenishment. 'Where do they put it?' they asked each other with wordless looks and smiles. Ah! These gentlefolk had a good dinner every day. How could they know the joy of eating their fill on the rare occasions when a chance occurred? There wasn't much riotous living for these poor people on fourteen shillings a week but, thank God, they knew how to enjoy anything that came their way – which was more than some of these bettermost folks could with their full stomachs made finicky and sickly with much over eating and drinking – poor things!

There was little or no talking until the diners had made serious headway into the splendid repast but with the second course a lighter mood prevailed, they paused for a good pull at their glasses of ale or cider. 'This is good stuff,' said one man to his neighbour across the table with the air of a connoisseur. 'Real stingo I calls it.'

'A-h-h! A diad sight different to that tackle you gets at Fox and Ounds,' agreed the other. 'I calls that dish wash now.'

'Whatever wer you a doing at the Fox an Ounds, I'd like to know?' chimed in a woman who was sitting near. 'A swallering that new frock your babby wants, I spose.'

'Oh I ent bin there since last Feast, an if I remembers rightly I only spent four pence then – so our bab bent lost many new frocks,' replied the second critic of beer good-humouredly.

'Fourpence buys a yard of good muslin or creponne,' persevered the woman teasingly. 'Alice could make him two frocks out of that, couldn't ee, Alice?'

'Than I could, Mrs Dan'll, a blue un an a pink un,' laughed the young wife who sat beside the man nursing an excessively fat baby. 'A-h-h well! It's a poor eart as never rejoices, I says, so I doon't begrudge im a pint at the Feast an such times – besides, our bab ud only a grown out on them frocks before now. So I bent a gooing to let that worrit me, that I bent.'

Well, nobody seemed to be worrying today, if they had cares – and who hadn't? They had been cast aside with blue slops, corduroys, and white aprons. Today was the day of peace and plenty and they were determined to enjoy every golden hour of it. Worry belonged to the past, and inevitably to the future, but for today there was a brief respite.

But here came the plum puddings – and plum puddings they were with a vengeance, inky black with sheer goodness. Each dish bore half a dozen full sized ones to be placed before each server, who made short work of them by deftly carving them into quarters and transferring them to the waiting plates to be drowned in luscious cream and passed down the table – many of the plates coming back for a second and even a third helping.

Except for the very few, who were either fine mouthed or extremely genteel, they had all eaten as much as they could comfortably – or uncomfortably, contain, tummies were distended and indigestion was rife, so that it was with a feeling of relief that they drew back a little from the table ready to listen to the speeches – but first of all Grace was played by the band and sung by all with genuine feeling, although in a somewhat low key – after so much feasting high notes were out of the question.

Squire, being the first gentleman in the immediate neighbourhood, had the first say. In his sharp thin voice he gave a little homily, the keynote of which was humility – his audience had had enough of being humble so didn't appreciate his sentiments very much especially when after a brief exhortation to honour God and the Queen, he dwelt lingeringly on their duty towards their 'Betters' nearer home. Some looked down their noses and some sniffed almost audibly.

Now it was the Parson's turn. As their much-criticised new Rector rose to address them, the somnolence that had been creeping over them completely disappeared. Their feud with him was the most exhilarating thing in their lives for here was someone whom they could not only get their teeth into – metaphorically, but who could fight back with all the subtle passes of the most accomplished mental boxer.

Now they found themselves laughing with great abandon, in spite of themselves, at his witticisms for he had a wonderful sense of humour. He had also a fine open countenance and a musical voice which was pleasing. He was too a brilliant scholar but that they never found him out in – to hold for or against.

His charm cut no ground with them – there was something ulterior behind it without a doubt. His clever cynicism, strange to say, they rather enjoyed – so long as it wasn't themselves who were the victims.

The old Rector who had shepherded them and their parents and grandparents for the last fifty years had died not long since. Gentle, homely and kind, he had been their guide, philosopher and friend with a vengeance. All their little pleasures, grievances and idiosyncrasies were an open book to him – and he had eyes to read. And now, this young 'flibberty gibbet' had come straight from Oxford to try his parsoning hand on them. Why he didn't even dress like a Parson! Tall and arrogant looking with his flashing blue eyes and strong white teeth visible when he smiled his slightly twisted and mocking smile, he wore a Norfolk suit with fancy stockings, or sometimes gaiters, and a Muller hat thrust back on his head, contrasting strangely with the exterior of their old friend, in his shovel hat and caped overcoat green with age, as he crept from cottage to cottage taking the most personal interest in all their doings, whether it was their children's clever sayings or what they'd had in the pot for supper. And now this young man had presumed to take his place – his place indeed!

He did no visiting and being a bachelor had no lady to deputise for him in this. When his parishioners were discussing him, as they often were, they were wont to say how much pleasure it would give them to drum him out of the parish – yet, they resented the time he spent out of it – wasn't he always careering off to play tennis or croquet with eligible young women in adjacent parishes, or riding or shooting or gadding off to Oxford or London?

Then he had made all sorts of meddlesome alterations in the times of services. They had always gone to church on Sunday afternoons, now they must go in the evenings and carry lanterns to light them through the fields and lanes – if they were to see and hear anything at all that was going on in the parish – for church was a rare place for news, little groups formed outside the churchyard gate after service and astonishing tales were then related. Then the Psalms must be sung. Sung indeed! When they had always been said as far back as memory went with clerk Tom's high falsetto voice dominant. Ancient institutions such as 'Mother's meetings' and 'Young Women's Monday Nights' were knocked on the head. The young men were handed over to the curate who in this sea of change was the only rock they had to cling to, and what with keeping the balance between the old regime and the new he sometimes, poor fellow, felt more like a tight rope walker than a rock. In the old Rector's time his duties had been many and of infinite variety, what with walking through snowdrifts almost up to his chin to take services in the tiny church of the sister parish in the winter, sitting up at nights with old men who were going, or were already gone, off their heads, hiving swarms of bees for old women or digging a bit of their garden for them, teaching in the night school, or walking the three miles into the town to buy, from his own meagre pocket money, a bottle of stuff for somebody's cough or collywobbles – in fact anything his hand found to do that he did right willingly. Now he had a new round of duties in addition to the old ones which he still did off his own bat. Added to all this he had to act as diplomat between the new Rector and his flock.

But today was a day of goodwill and that sentiment should for once be extended even to him their arch enemy. So they laughed at his sallies – although they were a bit doubtful at times as to what he was driving at, for they had become so accustomed to reading him back-wards, as it were. They gave three more resounding cheers when he had finished. All was forgiven – for the moment, and a short one for that – for now the band struck up once again with a piece called 'Jubilee' and composed by Mr Moore himself for the great occasion. The Rector set his teeth hard at first but when he could bear it no longer he clapped both hands over his ears – and so let loose a hornets nest above his head again after this briefest of respites.

Now the schoolchildren sang three little songs which the Governess had spared herself no pains in bringing to perfection during the past few weeks, and thus ended the musical part of the celebrations.

By this time the meal having settled somewhat, the youthful and energetic ones were becoming restive and anxious to be off to the next stage – although most of the elders and middle aged would fain have sat on a bit longer, for some of them could have done nicely with a comfortable snooze. The sports were to be held in the park about a mile away at the junction of three parishes all of which were joining forces, so as to make it a really big affair.

So now the very old and the very young were hoisted into the flower decked wagon, while the able bodied started off in twos and threes and half dozens on 'Shankses'. 'What was a mile to them? A mere flea bite,' they assured each other cheerfully although most of them had covered several miles already. What they didn't like much was 'Them bikes' which some of the youths were proudly possessed of 'Coming along behind a body so quiet like making them jump nearly out of their skins – they'd run everybody over before they'd done'. Bicycles were still something of a novelty here. No woman in the neighbourhood had one yet, although a year or two later several of them acquired second-hand ones and thus completely changed their way of life. But humble 'Shanks' was their only means of loco-motion for the present, unless it was an occasional hiring of Jim Ashton's donkey and cart to take or fetch their daughter's boxes from the three miles distant railway station – the girls of the village and hamlet went out to service directly they left school, most of them went to London – where they must have felt very lonely and forlorn in such a strange land. But after a brief sojourn there they lost their native dialect and acquired a mincing accent and a taste for smart clothes, both of which were very much admired by all when they returned to their native heath.

But the boys were a different matter – they stayed at home and were made darlings of, nothing was too good for them. Mother screwed and scraped to save a few shillings to add to their savings that they might have concertinas, mouth organs, and just now, bicycles – the sisters in service were invariably looked to, to make up the required amount from their very small wages. Never and nowhere was the young male so highly honoured as then and there. Father had had his day – 'When young cocks begin to crow tis time for the old uns to be quiet,' they were apt to say – in a very few short years these youths would themselves be the husbands and fathers of the parish – and very good ones too, in spite of mother's pandering.

So the young favourites raced up and down the dusty road on their bright new bicycles causing the walkers to jump about like eels to get out of their way, and much laughter and nonsense was the outcome.

As they neared the park they began to fall in with merrymakers from the other two villages, there was a reunion of old friends and neighbours and distant relatives, some of whom they hadn't met for years, so the last lap of their journey was enlivened by greetings, chaffings, or condolences, as the case might require, varied by vivid descriptions of the bounteous feast they had lately disposed of and their present reactions to same.

Now their Mecca was reached they all settled down again to deliberately enjoy themselves.

'Us be out to joy ourselves'

The park, a natural one and well wooded, had been lent for the day by its owner, a super Squire of the neighbourhood, for his humbler neighbours to disport themselves in while he himself sought diversion elsewhere – in paying personal homage to the Queen no doubt. He had locked his door and taken the key – otherwise the freedom of his domain was bequeathed upon them. The grass was cool and green to walk upon and the pleasant shade of beech and oak were greatly pleasing to the company after their hot walk on stony roads. The gardens too were open for their delight, and that part of the park nearest to them had been prepared for the sports – the grass here was clean shaven and gaily decorated farm wagons were arranged around to act as grandstands that all who so wished could rest and admire at their ease. Gay banter flew from wagon to wagon as the company took their seats. Strings of pennants criss-crossed between trees, and in the shadiest corner of all, a long table was spread with bunting and arranged with glasses and cups and saucers ready to be filled from the large glass containers of lemon and orangeade that sparkled so delightfully, or the hissing copper tea urn. Free drinks for the men were housed in a small marquee at the opposite side of the course.

The races were announced through a megaphone – a novelty which at first caused much amusement. The children came first with all the old favourites such as 'Potato Picking', 'Hobbled Horses', 'Egg and Spoon' etc. etc., even the losers left the arena with a smile for they were given bright new Jubilee pennies to salve their disappointment. Soon victors and vanquished were dashing like wild Indians in and out of the crowd of onlookers in games of their own making, or bursting their little tummies around the refreshment stall with glass after glass of fizzy lemon kali – the first, and last time no doubt, that they were able to drink to their hearts content of that delectable concoction.

Sounds of great merriment now came from the race course. Old George Sairn was shuffling along to the starting point, followed by the laughter and cheers of the whole assembly, in answer to the trumpet voice asking boys of ten to come forward and show their mettle. The bigwigs in command looked him over with mock gravity and some of them said solemnly 'Come, Come! You can't be ten years old yetawhile, young man. Now tell me pray when was your tenth birthday?'

'Sixty years agone last Sunday as ever wus,' piped the old man. 'That wer at Coronation gooins on. Me Dad he bet me a penny as ow I udn't beat young Jim Ayres in that there race for ten year olds and I wus countermined I ud – just to show im. I won the prize that I did and I be a going to win it now. What I sez is – if old Queen, and she be nine years older, be game to racket all around London town today, well, I baint dead yet neither.'

A few boys of from ten to eleven years had come forward too. Now a bevy of strapping youths in their teens and early twenties, the gayest of the gay, determined on a spree. There was a little conference behind old George's back, and then the signal for starting was given.

Old George came in first at a snail's gallop with all the others, puffing and panting and mopping brows, behind doing a standstill run. The cheering was deafening as he received the half crown prize from the judges and this the young men insisted on doubling with contributions of twopences and threepences from their own pockets. They then carried him back to his seat in the wagon grandstand amidst long and loud applause.

'I told ee I ud, now didn't I?' he cried triumphantly to his cronies as soon as he had recovered his breath.

'Ah-h! There you be!' replied one of them thoughtfully. 'In ten minutes you've become master of as much money as 'Parish' ull give ee in a fortnight?'

'Ee adn't better jingle it too loud,' advised another, 'or 'Parish' ull think ee doon't want nothing for the next fortnight.'

The victor's face became somewhat clouded as this difficulty was presented to him. 'Ee'd better goo on spree and spend it, George, then none can take it away from ee.'

The old man looked amazed. 'Spend it,' he gasped. 'All at one goo! I've never spent more nor sixpence at a sittin on flightiness in all me born days – that I ent.'

'Well, look out that there Relieving Officer chap doon't get to know on it.'

'What did ee buy we that alf crown ee won at Coronation? Doon't ee remember? T'want on skittles I do ope – at that young age.'

George wandered off into the past for a moment and came back full of animation. 'Ah-h – now I comes to think on it,' said he, 'I mind the fust thing I done was to give me mother sixpence to buy a flower to goo in er Sunday bonnet – a bunch a lilies o the valley that she ad bin anchoring after – an I mind ow she wur as plazed as punch we um. Me dad I bought a bit o bacca for – that wer threepence. Then I give all me young sisters and brothers – ther wer six on um, a apenny apiece to spend on lollipops. There wer a shilling gone ang before I knowed wher I wer.' Old George became lost in thoughts of the past.

'Come on now,' encouraged one of his listeners, 'You ent told us what you did we tother eighteen pence. You ent got it now in that stocking, av ee?'

The old financier brought back the gaze of his watery blue eyes from far away youth. 'Ah-h, I mind now, I went to Banbury market fur the fust time in me life. Old Gaffer White – as I worked for, wus a sendin a wagon full o someat or tother an ee said as how I might goo to old osses. The Market wer swarmed we folks, I'd never sin the likes on it in all me life. Then the stalls we all sorts o things and cheap Jacks kicking up such a clatter – I thought I should goo deaf that I did.

'Well, after a bit the man who wer we me said ee'd old osses ees self while I ad a look round – I can't mind who he wer now,' the old man showed signs of meandering off into the past again to search for the man's name but his listeners hauled him back to finish his tale.

'Well, I went round cautious like for I didn't mean to let um get me money out o me afore I'd sin the best articles. Anyhow, I comes to a man what as piles o cord breeches laying beside him. "What price be them?" asked I. "Oh any price you like," ses ee. "Now ere's a nice pair just your fit, young squire," and he olds up a nice pair o cords what ud a done me just a treat. "They might," I said rather offhand.

"Or praps you'd better ave um a bit bigger so that they'd serve you in a year or twos time when you've growed somewhat – for depend on it these breeches ull never wear out, cast iron thats what they be made on. What do you say for um? alf a crown?"

'Me eart sunk like a stone – for I desired them breeches above everything, just like the men's breeches they wer and now I wus at work I thought meself a man and wanted to look like one, that I did. The tears cum up in me eyes so I looked down on the ground and shook me ead. Several folks gathered round and some on um bought pairs – the man put the pair ee ad showed me on one side and when they ad gone again he said to me kind like, "Well, I'll take two shillings me lad." I shook me ead again and he sold a pair to somebody else as cum along. "How much ave ee got to spend?" he asked me. "Only a shillin," said I for I was countermined to keep sixpence, come what might, to spend on some o the good things to eat that the market wer busting we.

'The man whistled at that, but after a minute or two ee said, "All right, lad, take um," an ee rolled um up in a bit o paper and I gen im me shillin an went off before ee ad a chance o altering ees mind.

'I still ad me sixpence, so seein a ooman sellin ogpuddins I bought a length to take ome for our supper – they wer threepence. The last threepence I spent on a nice big bag o brandysnaps to eat gooing back – Ah-h! Them wer brandysnaps! I can taste um now. They baint made like that now, that um baint.'

The old men and women continued to discuss the past – what fun they had in those days – or so they thought looking back, all the trials and tribulations were mercifully forgotten – it was like stirring up a bowl of pot pouri, only the fragrance remained – the roses which compose it have for ever lost their thorns, the bitter scent of aromatic herbs is no more.

But while these elders had been calling back the past the present was in full flow judging by the signs of excitement that came from the race course – young men had surmounted almost unsurmountable barriers in the obstacle race, young women had done ridiculous things. Now the greasy pole is in progress – a huge home cured ham is firmly fixed to a long stout pole the other end of which is planted in the ground, and all and sundry are invite to climb up to get the ham, for if they can reach it, it is theirs but, and here's the snag, the pole is plastered with grease and it is not so easy as it looks to the uninitiated. Young men look up at the ham enviously and then down at their spruce Sunday suits – is it worth while? There are but few entrants until the curate comes panting up from somewhere and says he has acquired several old pairs of trousers – they are in the beer tent if any of the men would like to go and pop on a pair to try their luck in. This simplified matters considerably and now all the young men and some of the older ones are anxious to try their prowess. But it was a tricky undertaking – some made but poor climbers while others got almost to the top and when within an ace of their object slid down to the ground like stones, to the amusement of lookers on. There was great hilarity throughout the whole event and at last when a most persevering competitor did succeed his valour was applauded as it simply deserved. Many were the applicants for invitations to dinner on the Sunday on which the ham was boiled, to which the hero laughingly replied that it wasn't going to be boiled on a Sunday but fried on a Monday – for which sally he received fresh cheers.

'Ent there going to be no greasy pig?' queried an old woman in a cackly voice. 'Us ad one last time. It doon't seem right an prapper we out one, that it doon't.'

'There was one at our last Jumliee,' said a youngish woman from another village. 'I remember it well because my brother was on the church tower which overlooked the sports field and just as it was starting he thought he saw me in the running, so down he swarmed in such a tare intending to haul me home by the hair of me head and then shut me up in cellar for so disgracing myself – and him. But, of course, it wasn't me and we had a good laugh.'

'I want to know why there ent one today?' demanded the old woman.

'Well to tell the truth, Granny,' shouted a middle aged woman in her ear, 'Us be all getting too genteel for such goings on.'

'Genteel!' scoffed the old woman. 'Well, I spose you may ride the igh oss on your mens big wages. My old man worked nearly all his life for eight shillin a wik and us ad eleven children to set gooin in the world. Now your men gets fourteen, every man jack on um – enow to keep a regi-ment o sojors on I sez.'

The women laughed and one of them shouted again in the old woman's ear, 'Ave ee eared as ow Bell ere be gooin to buy erself a carriage and pair?'

'Anyhow, what is this greasy pig old Grannie Grunt is talking about? A pig stuck on a pole?' asked a young woman who had come as a servant to one of the big houses from Birmingham, and was now a bride.

'You mean to say you never heard on one, Mrs Titmarsh?' replied one of her neighbours incredulously – 'These town folk they didn't know anything!' 'Well tis a little half grown pig plastered we grease and let loose in about a pole o ground whats bin urdled off we the women what goo in for it runnin im round and round like mad and the one as catches im as im.'

The bride was impressed 'I wish they'd have one today,' she said longingly. 'I'd lay hold of im I bet.'

'It was a nasty horrid sport and I'm glad they have done away with it,' said the one who had told of her brother being so angry when he thought she had stopped to join in such savagery. 'I couldn't abear to hear the poor little beast squealing as if he would go crazy with all those women scrobbling and screaming like lunatics after him. And yet I've seen some of the bettermost folks laughing their heads off as if it was fine fun.'

'You can afford to be proud on fourteen shillings a wick,' croaked the old woman who had been straining her ears to catch the conversation. 'If you ad to do we eight you'd a bin glad to catch anything and it udn't a urt them fine feelings o yourn if y betters ad a laughed at y, that it udn't.'

'Betters indeed!' scoffed one woman. 'T'would ave done um far more credit to have cried at such gooins on.'

'Poor old gal!' said another of the group kindly. 'All in all she's ad a ardish time on it. Although I must say she didn't lose much when she lost er old man. And er daaters ent much better – I should think it was a good thing she lost all but them two as little uns, saved er many a tear in the long run I'll warrant.'

'Makes er a bit spiteful to see us a bit better off,' agreed another. 'Not but what us couldn't do we a bit more, that us could.'

So they helped the disagreeable woman to the pleasantest seat under the trees and bought her cups of tea and answered all her cross-ness with kindly patience.

This was a space for recuperation and reminisences. Friends who had not met for many a long day sat side by side in the shade of the chestnuts discussing news old and new. Choice bits of scandal which had been stored up in their minds were brought out and aired. Details of hard confinements were discussed between women with great relish – courtships and marriages with all the exciting little snippets of gossip which surround them, and deaths with all the morbid facts and fancies were told in detail.

Most of the men had migrated to the beer tent where good ale was flowing freely – even those who were looked upon as teetotallers were drinking the sparkling amber fluid with great enjoyment.

'Why I allus took you for a strict T.T., Alf,' jollied a big man with a rust coloured face.

'I be,' replied the little fair man with his blue eyes twinkling. 'When I as to pay for it I be a strict T.T.'

The conversation here was very subdued at first – laconic questions and answers about crops and animals amongst which they worked, or about their own or neighbours allotments. But as the beer began to work itself to the brain they waxed boastful and began to relate mirac-ulous feats of strength, or the fabulous size and weight of the pig they had reared, the growth of peas and beans which rivalled those of 'Jack and the Beanstalk' fame, the words of wisdom they had uttered only to be disregarded by so and so, when to have heeded them would have averted the direst catastrophies.

Mr Moore brought forth a banjo and began to play and sing some slightly naughty little songs at which the audience laughed roister-ously. Others, who had a voice – and some who hadn't, obliged with a song. All were steeped in the warmth and jollity of life.

Presently some of those who wished for a breath of fresh air, or some activity, went out for a game of quoits on the grass. The iron rings were worn thin by generations of players – they were probably being thrown for the last time, for after that game, which had in the past decade only been played on rare occasions, was lost in oblivion.

Courting couples wandered far afield in the park and woods, forgetting and forgotten by their little world until they again appeared for the dancing. Upon the lake in the far distance a boat drifted lazily – Governess and Curate had at last escaped from the chains which bound them in their manifold duties.

In the gardens little groups roamed or sat on seats and talked, when they were tired of admiring the flowers and layout, or watched the fountain at play and the goldfish frisking in the pond. Mothers, trying desperately hard to keep their children together under their own eye, walked round and round the broad gravel walks looking for all the world like little hen partridges surrounded by their coveys. Some of them even dared to peep through the long windows, of which there were seven, into the drawing room of the mansion and gaze wistfully at the blue brocaded furniture, luxurious carpet, and gleaming grand piano. Most of them sighed to be rich.

'Oh, I'm not so sure that rich folk are always happy any more than we are,' said the sensible woman of the party. 'I'd be quite content as I am if I could get a new jacket and frock all round for the children without pinching and screwing.'

'Oh, goo on!' laughed her companion, 'Why not say one for yourself while you be about it!'

'What would you ave if you could ave anything you wished for, Mrs Dibben?' asked another neighbour who had joined them.

So they fell to wishing for the most incongruous things, then laughed themselves to tears for having thought of such silly things. One wanted the grand piano they had just seen, though she hadn't a note of music in her, also it would have entirely filled the living room of her tiny cottage.

'You and Tom and the chuldern ad all ave to live in the wood – as for there ud be no room for you in the ouse,' said one and they all laughed again at the thought.

'Well, I should like a horse, a beautiful high stepping chestnut, for it's always been the height of my ambition to go hunting,' said the erstwhile sensible woman.

'Wherever should you keep im?' queried the others.

'Oh, he'd have to lie down flat under my bed when I wasn't out hunting.'

'I,' said the third woman, who was very short and very fat, and had ten children, 'I should like a beautiful gold brocade gown we a long train – I've never ad a new frock since I was married, then it was only me last Sunday un, titivated up a bit we bows and things, since then I've ad to catch as catch can, so I should like a real smart un for once.'

Fresh peals of laughter greeted this – the idea of Bell trailing around her humble abode in her grand dress was too much. 'We be just laughing at our own folly, that us be,' said one as she wiped her eyes.

But tragedy followed fast upon comedy – at that moment there was a chorus of squeals and cries for help and the women ran helter skelter to find one of their children, all of whom had wandered back to the fish, and while their mother's minds had been given to foolish fancies, had fallen in. Fortunately she had been rescued by a bystander, and was wet and blubbering but quite unharmed. All the other children were weeping too.

The poor little hen of a mother was distracted at the sight of so much water. It was a hot day and twenty years later the procedure would have been quite simple – to have stripped the child of her wet clothes and let her run about in the sunshine while they dried – a handerkerchief doing duty for raiment in the meantime. But life wasn't so casual then-a-days. Everyone within earshot had run towards the pond on hearing the children's cries and were now thrusting advice upon the worried mother.

'Take her home straight away before she catches her death of cold,' advised some.

But the mother rather jibbed at that – she had been looking forward to the frolics of the evening herself – besides there were four miles to walk to get home – not to mention the other children who would be bitterly disappointed at losing their rides on the wooden horses, the music of which was at that very moment beginning to reach their ears. Anyway, she couldn't just stand here and watch the child drip.

One of the audience produced a first aid outfit in the shape of a paper of peppermints which acted like magic, not only upon that wet child but upon the dry ones also, who were still a bit tearful from their fright. This gave the mother pause to gather the few scattered wits which were left to her, after bearing and rearing ten children.

'Come on our Ede,' she said with the air of one who was used to dealing with the movement of armies, so taking the child by the hand, and followed by her cronies and a troupe of the other children, she walked firmly towards what looked like a secluded corner.

Four-years-old Edith was quickly stripped of her numerous garments, and her small body dried – all the handkerchiefs that could be mustered were commandeered for this purpose. Meanwhile several of the other children had been partly undressed and one article of dress taken from each wherewith to redress small Edith; as they wore at least three petticoats this wasn't difficult, especially as some of these petticoats were frocks of yesterday. Still the mothers felt anxiety lest any of them should feel the miss of a garment and catch cold!

The wet clothes were hung out to dry on one of the garden seats – this arrangement had one drawback – someone must stay there to mind them, so they could not all go together to the fair, that was now going on full blast in the part of the park which had been dedicated to it. So they agreed to take turns. All being unselfish by nature, or having learnt the virtue in a hard school, each of them insisted on being the one to keep the first vigil.

'You goo on, you two, I'll stay behind,' said the first.

'No you won't, I will,' said the second.

'That you won't – narn on you. I be gooin to stay and that's flat,' said the third – and being the strongest willed of the trio she stayed while the other two went off with their numerous offspring to enjoy the fun.

Only a few people, those who liked to take their pleasures quietly, were left in the garden. Mrs Dan'll perched on one end of the seat fell into a reverie – it was a rare thing for her to be sitting with her hands before her doing nothing, although she had but four children – a small family compared with some of her neighbours, not that families were quite as large now as they had been in her childhood –

she had been one of twelve herself. And hers were getting off hand, the youngest seven years old. Still, she was always on the go from morning till night, what with washing, cooking, and cleaning, tending the pig when they had one, and a few hens, and helping Dan a bit with the garden and allotment, besides which she had lately taken to going out washing and ironing two days a week at a farm-house two miles from her home. What pleasure it was to have a shilling or two of her own earning to buy a few little extras with – this had put her on another plane altogether in her own estimation, there was that bit of bright coloured coconut matting for the floor, which had completely revolutionised her cottage, then that bit of stuff for a new white frock for Mayday for Ruth, as nice a one, or better, than anyone else's child had. Or, and this her greatest delight, to give young Will a sixpence to spend as he liked, not to mention the bicycle she was helping him to save for secretly. So with all her activities, it was rarely she had time to sit and think, and what would she have made of this unique occasion had it been prolonged, it was hard to say for just then a figure loomed upon her horizon which made her sit bolt upright and gaze in pleased astonishment.

'Why! If it ent Queenie!' she exclaimed going forward and grasping the old woman by the hand. 'How be you, me poor old gal? Come on now, tell me all about it.' And she cleared a space on the seat for her to sit down.

Queenie wiped away the tear which the warm greeting had brought to her eye. Her face was brown and wrinkled like a nutmeg, she wore a voluminous dress of thick brown stuff, the short cape and little close fitting bonnet of the workhouse.

Before she could recover sufficiently to speak about herself, pointing to the drying clothes she asked with evident curiosity, 'You ent bin an bought your washing we you, ave ee, Liza?'

'No. I bent so workish as all that, that I bent, Queenie.' And Mrs Dan'll briefly explained the meaning of what looked like her own industry. 'But I wants to ear all about yourself, Queenie. How do you like being in the big house? And how come you ere?'

'Well, I be ere because our Ben fetched me out for the jollifications, I be gooin to stop a wick we im, that I be. Ed'd ave me for good but

Eliza Massey (known as Queenie) spent her last years in the workhouse at Bicester. Here she is photographed in 1880 wearing the workhouse uniform. (Photo courtesy of Eva Bateman)

they wunt let im as long as me old man's alive in the big ouse, guardians sez if one be there so must tother. An nobody could make do we the old man – clane off is ead now that ee be.'

'Well, it serves im right, that it do, for ee wus a old gallus,' replied Mrs Dan'll. 'So it ent no manner o use you standing up for im to me. Do ee get a bit o snuff for I know you be main fond of a pinch.'

'That us do, everyone as takes snuff as alf ounce and them as don't as a paper o lollipops. Looked well after us be – enough to eat, and these nice frocks to wear, an a clean chimee an all that every wick. I feel alf in eaven sometimes after all I went through we the old man. I doon't spose ee allus knowed what ee wus about,' added Queenie in feeble defence of her absent lord.

'Ee knowed alright. Ee med be off is ead now but ee wurdn't allys, depend on it.'

'Tis alright now me dear – ee don't trouble me at all – men and women be kept each to emselves, the nuss takes me to see im once a wick and that be all. I bent a mite miserable – our Ben and tothers ull fetch me out as soon as ought appens to im. Not but what I miss me old cat though, an me bees, and the few gillyflowers an pinks in me garden – them belonged to me and us ent got anything belonging to us there, that us ent.'

'A-h-h! Many's the times I've sin you sittin in the sun taking your pinch o snuff when I wur a little gal. An ow you used to tang that key on the shovel when your bees wer a swarmin.'

'I never lost a swarm ever,' said the old woman proudly. 'A-h-h! Them pinks and gillyflowers an the bit o sweetbriar did smell nice,' she added with a sigh.

'I've nicked one or two on em many a time when I wur a gal, an wanted a posy to stick in me Sunday frock. Me mother ud a gen me a good iding if she'd a knowed.'

'She brought you up to be straightforad, that she did, I mind ow she used to say "I larn my chuldern not to take a pin what doon't belong to em." But flowers be different, bent um? Somhow I felt plazed for you to covet my pinks – I sin you pick one many a time then you'd jump round the corner out o sight like lightenin.'

They laughed themselves to tears over this, and before they had finished wiping their eyes, one of the other mothers came panting back to take the watch over the damp clothes, but as the lovers were beginning to stroll back through the gardens on their way to the lawn where the dancing was soon to begin, it was deemed by the old watcher and the new to be in questionable taste to display such personal garments – though so small, to their innocent eyes. So they were swept together and tied in a neat bundle to be borne off by Bell who was anxious to get back to her progeny before further harm befell them. Evening was beginning to fall.

'Us be only just beginning to get warmed up,' declared one of the olduns.

'No, us ent begun enjoying ourselves yet an that's a fact,' agreed a young one in passing.

'Come on, Rose me dear, I be gooin to ave a dance we ee' piped the old man to a bonny young girl.

'That you shall, Master Blinkow,' replied Rose heartily. 'I hope old Sally Barnes won't be jealous though.'

'That old bag o bones! Legs like sparrows! Why, I'd goo to

Blenheim steps an swear me life agen um if they wer mine, that I ud!
I likes um nice an plump like you me dear.'

'You'm thinking you be back at that Coronation – a young chap
agen, we all the girls round ee like bees round a oney pot, I'll
warrant,' said the young man good humouredly.

'A-h-h! An us got up to some pranks in them days – as full o
mischief as a cat be full o airs, us wer. Nothin goos on nowadays.
Young men bent young men no more.'

'They baint old women anyhow,' laughed young Walter as he
hastened his step to catch up with Rose. 'If you doubts my words just
you take note of what goos on under them fairy lamps tonight.'

'And joy ourselves us ull!'

The gardens began to look as if they were inhabited by myriads of fireflies, for every one of the thousand fairylamps had by now been hand lit by industrious gardeners, the result was a veritable fairyland in which almost anything might be expected to happen. On the lawn dancing had already begun to the music of two, or was it three?, violins. The young couples, fresh from the woods and fields, wearing romance like an almost visible veil through which they saw no one but each other, were moving dreamily in an old fashioned waltz in which a few more sophisticated dancers joined in with more briskness. Older people sat around and watched – some wistfully, others with envy deploring that their dancing days were done, and thinking what fine capers they would cut were they young again. One or two of the old men who had been beaux in their youth took a turn with their daughters or good natured young neighbours.

One young man – the very pick of the basket of masculine comeliness, left his partner and came over to where Queenie was sitting with several of her old friends and neighbours, and taking her hand would have led her off to the next dance – but Queenie demurred.

'Oh come on, me dear' said he coaxingly. 'Why, tis only seemly you should have a dance tonight the same as you did at the Queen's coronation – you be named after er too, and tis said you wer born on the same day, and married likewise.'

'I may a bin, tis true, but lork-a massy young Charlie, I couldn't dance now to save me life it ud make me giddy as a goose, that it ud.'

'Come, doon't ee be faint earted Queenie,' encouraged some of the other sitters out. 'They be just a gooin to start the "Keel Row", now doon't ee tell us you ent danced that when your legs were younger than they be today.'

'I ent a gooin to now, anyhow – cutting such a foolish figure at my age – besides making meself bad.'

'That's right, Queenie,' said a reputed humourist in the audience. 'Doon't ee goo wasting all that good vitals you've et today.' This raised a general laugh.

'I never did see as much vitals, never in all me born life,' said Queenie thoughtfully. 'A-h-h! ther wunt much about at one time. A few turnup tops wer all I could get we a bit o bread for my chuldern's dinner many a time.'

'A-h-h! You've ad a ard row to hoe, poor old gal! That you ave,' said a younger woman kindly. 'A different lot to our Queen's – t'is queer when you comes to think on it, ow different folkses lots be cast. Now udn't it a bin funny, you bein born same day, if you'd bin er and she'd bin you. What should you a done?'

'I should a stayed wer I wus, an wer I wusn't urtin nobody – in me own ouse,' said Queenie promptly. 'I might a ad another ive or two o bees, an I should ave ad a nice bit of bacon for me dinner every day and a bit o butcher's meat a Sundays.'

'Now't else?' asked her inquisitor. 'What about a carriage an pair? an servants to wait on ee?'

'I could never ave got used to anything like that,' replied the old woman a little disdainfully.

'A-h-h well!' sighed another. 'I don't doubt, but what our Queen as ad er ups and downs same as the rest on us – only us doon't know nothing about um – it must be main lonely for er bein so igh up – we nobody quite good enough to make a neighbour on, nobody to spake to as you might say.'

'She lost a good usband – that us do know,' said one. 'That wer a bad goo.'

'A-h-h! The good uns always goos afore their time,' sighed another.

'And the bad uns always stays to torment ee all yer life – like me, don't um, Jen?' put in her husband. This turned sighs into laughter once more.

'Come for a walk round the gardens?' invited Mrs Dan'll when she found herself standing beside Mrs Tuffrey – not that she wanted the company of that cantankerous old besom, but seeing her all alone here her heart was touched, and today of all days was the time to extend good fellowship even to the most unloved.

'Ent um just enjoying emselves!' she said by way of opening conversation as they left the dancers behind. 'Our Nell dances lovely, doon't she?' Nell was her young unmarried sister.

Mrs Tuffrey sniffed. 'Dancing is a devil's pastime an answerable for all sorts o sins,' she said in a deep voice. 'What, I say, wus your Nell a dooin of in that spinney we Charlie all arternoon? Up to someat, I vow.'

'Our Nell knows ow to behave herself better n you can tell er,' said Mrs Dan'll shortly – this put Mrs Tuffrey somewhat in her place. 'I doon't know as theres much arm in a few kisses,' she said pacifically. 'They leads up to weddings, anyhow.'

She was instantly forgiven. 'Now doon't the flower beds look pretty we all them coloured lights on em?' Mrs Dan'll asked. 'Makes me think of Crystal Palace – not as I've ever sinit, only eard talk on it by them that as. Us doon't see nothing in country places. They do say if you've never bin to London you'll die a fool.'

'London is a sinful place, folks dressed up in their Sunday clothes all the time and merrymaking gooin on from one year's end to tother, and their souls gooin eadlong into damnation.'

'As fur as I can make out it's alright for them as as plenty o money to jingle in their pockets, but a poor look out for them what hasn't,' said Mrs Dan'll. 'I read in a book about two poor little orphans that slept on doorsteps an under arches on bitter cold nights, an nobody took um in or give um a crust to eat. If that's ow they goo on in London I'd rather stay where I be, even if us doon't see the sights. Us udn't ave let them little mites goo cold an ungry, but there, they say you doon't even know your next door neighbour in London.'

'An a good thing too, I should say, if they're anything like my neighbour – a real good for nothing besom that she is. Now what do you think – tother day if she didn't goo and throw er soapsuds down so they run all down my path and then to cap it all – '

A lusty howl interrupted what would have been a long and unpleasant story.

'If that ent our young Ruth I'll eat my at!' said Mrs Dan'll stepping briskly forward, and sure enough a small forlorn creature came running towards her.

'What's the matter, my duck?' enquired her mother anxiously.

'Young Cissie Moore as bin an broke my squeaking lamb what I won on the shies!'

'Well, she didn't do it a purpose I doon't spose, did she now? And anyhow, whats the use a ballin like that? Anybody ud think you'd lost your ead, that um ud.'

'She did do it a purpose,' sobbed Ruth. 'She said she ud and she snatched it away from me an stamped er foot on it.'

'A-h-h! But what ad you bin an done to er? Someat I know.'

Ruth was silent at that; she had no desire to tell the other side of the story, so she dried her eyes with the handkerchief that was pinned with a safetypin underneather her frock, and tried to think of something to say to change the conversation.

'Shall us ave another Jubilee next year, Mum?'

'No, my duck, us shant. I don't spose us shall ever ave another one.'

'Mum, can I ave another goo in the swingboats? Cos us ent never going to ave another Jubilee.'

'Oh goo on, you old coaxer! Ere's a penny for you. And mind you doon't goo upsettin anybody else's applecart or I'll upset yourn next time. Come straight back – I'll sit on this ere seat an wait for you.'

The child ran off happily – determined to make the most of the one Jubilee she was sure of, the mother watching her go, laughed within herself at her child's little vagaries, thinking of them – as mothers alone do, as engaging little ways. During this interlude Mrs Tuffrey had sauntered on and met with someone else with whom she was now discussing the sins and shortcomings of others with great enjoyment. Mrs Dan'll gave a sigh of relief. Two other women came along both of whom she had known in her childhood, so they sat together on the seat and talked old times, and laughed uproariously as each reminded each of small inconsequent happenings. Ruth came running back obediently (for strange though it may seem today there was once a time when children obeyed their parents) and they all once more dissolved themselves in the crowd that edged the lawn.

But the hour was waxing late, gradually the dancers fell out of dance, the musicians packed up their violins ready to depart, mothers began to seek and find their progeny, fathers, still merry or exceedingly wise, reunited themselves with their families.

But there were still the fireworks – the grand climax of the day. At ten o'clock the first rocket went up, tired children rallied as if by magic giving little squeals of delight as one followed another into the sky – but these were nothing to those which followed – fountains of golden fire and all sorts of wonderful set pieces, each one better and better, working to a grand crescendo with a picture of the good old Queen herself, and this the signal for the National Anthem.

And so homeward.

But wonders had not yet ceased and another was revealed to them before they had travelled half the length of the carriage road which led them out of the park into the roadway. Under the tall beech trees, like jewels scattered recklessly on the grass, a thousand tiny lights shimmered in the moonlight. There was a chorus of exclamation notes from the women and children, and even the men contributed some pleased grunts.

'What be um, Mum. What be um?' cried one little girl – and remembering the tragedy of her own string of blue glass beads – 'Ave some lady bin and broke the string of er diamante necklace?'

'A-h-h, maybe,' laughed her mother, 'and she wur too proud to stoop to pick um up, seemingly. No, my duck, them be glow worms.'

'Worms!' echoed the child. 'Them nasty things! How do um come to look so pretty and shiny looking? They can't be worms, can um?'

One of the men of the group – who in his own opinion, was a bit of a scientist – in the opinion of his cronies, a regular old know-all – began to explain in a roundabout fashion why glow worms glowed but got so involved that by the time he had finished nobody was listening and the glow worms were left far behind. They would have been forgotten if two of the elder children had not run and picked up several each, and arranged them button wise down the front of their dresses, and so carried them all the way home.

At the park gates there were 'Good Nights' and plenty of humorous advice given to those going in the opposite direction. The fun was not over yet – far from it. The walk home was as full of mirth as it could well be – tired but by no means weary they set out with right good will in little groups within hailing distance of each other. The youngest of families in Mother's arms while Father carried the next in size pick-a-back, big sisters and brothers giving a bandy-chair now and then to rest smaller ones, the old ones helped along by any who had a free arm.

The young men and maidens had disappeared – 'Gone by the short cut the longest way round!' laughed one of the elders when their absence was noticed.

'And I told our Emly not to goo across them fields a daggling er long tail on that wet grass – a pretty daggletail she'll be!' said Emily's mother crossly.

'You know right well, Lizzie, it ent nar a mossel o use tellin um anything at that stage – ther youngness drives um on like a ragin fire to ave ther own way. An ther own way they'll ave come what may. You wer same when you wer young and green I'll be bound.'

'That, I never wer,' denied Emily's mother. 'All this wilfulness as come about we this batch o young uns, I doon't know whatever the world's comin to, that I doon't.'

'Now Liz!' spoke up a man from the rear of the group. 'You ent forgot when you went a dappling in the dew across them selfsame fields on night after arvest-ome merrymakings we me – I doon't know ow it come about – you must a inticed me somehow.'

'Aye, I do seem to remember someut, that I do, Amos.' Liz stood stock still to let her memory work. 'Howsomeever, t'wer before Jim begun a courting me, or Jane ad thoughts on you – that I'll swear,' this to placate any little shade of jealousy in her own husband or Amos's wife who were both present.

'Well, you as to taste en try before you buy – as the saying is,' put in Liz's quiet little husband good humouredly. 'Thats only jonic, that is.'

'I can't for the life of me think what I wer doing gooin ome we you, Amos. It wusn't as if I ever fancied you, that I never.'

'An I never fancied you neither, Liz,' replied Amos with the same candour. 'I remember ow you lingered on them stiles though, I thought us should never get ome – an your mother ud be after us we the copper stick any minute. There us sat staring at the moon like a pair o moonstruck cows.'

Lizzie's husband gave an amused little snort – he was thinking, 'What a rum goo it ud bin if our Liz ad got old on Amos stead o me!' and Amos's wife thought, 'My! What fireworks ther'd a bin if our Amos ad got itched up we old Liz – all of a splutter like ot fat both on um.'

Someone walking in front called back to them, 'Ther they goo! Look! – see um?'

'A-h-h!, so they be,' agreed some of those behind, craning their necks, but one or two were either shortsighted or were not endowed with enough imagination to see what the others saw. 'Tusmer lights!' snorted one of these disdainfully. 'Some folks can see what ther ent ther to see. Tis all my eye and Betty Martin!'

But those who had eyes that saw kept them intently fixed upon the road which ran to an angle with the one they were traversing, and there sure enough were two bright lights moving forward to a certain point then retreating at the same pace.

'Now you'll see,' said one of the watchers. 'When they get to the big gates they'll disappear into the drive that leads up to the mansion.'

'But they'll come back,' said another, 'and goo on like that all night.'

'T'is a curious thing' said another, 'but it's bin gooin on for years – me Grannie used to see um when she was a bit of a gal. They doon't show every night mind, but only now and agen.'

'I've sin um all times o night when I've bin up we lambs,' remarked Shepherd Sampson.

'You mind that night old Sam Watts took bad and died – I went to town to fetch Doctor – about two o'clock in mornin it wer, an there they wer a dancing up an down road as merry as mummers.'

'Ad to goo mightly close to um too, didn't ee Joe? I reckon the sweat wer a tricklin down yer back, wurdn't it?'

'I beant afrit on um – nor any ghosts as fur as that goos,' boasted Joe.

'The only chap as I know on who as bin right up close to um wus oilman. It wus dark when ee'd finished is round one winter's day an ee as to goo that way to get back to Fritell. Ee wasn't a thinkin a word about them lights till ee wus right a top on um, as you might say. Ee wus jog trotting along, as easy as you like, when all on a sudden the road in front was all afire. Is oss wer frit to death an udn't budge another step, not but what ee wusn't as scared as a crow imself, but ee ad to jump out an old er ead while ee led er down the grass verge to a field gate that wur andy, thinking to imself that ee'd stop ere at a safe distance while ee waited to see what wus gooin to appen next. But when ee looked back to the road all ee could see wur a carriage drivin along towards the big gates, an it adn't passed im – that ee swore. If that wusn't a ghost carriage I doon't know what wus.'

'Ghosts!' said one of the unbelievers vehemently. 'Only fools believe in ghosts.'

'Well,' said the sensible woman whose word always carried weight. 'There's always some explanation to all strange things that happen, if folks only looked deeper into them.

'Course ther is,' said the scientist. 'Now them lights be just Jenny Bumtails, you mark my words.'

'Them Jenny Bumtails – some calls um Jack-a-lanterns, some Will-o-wisps, whatever you likes to call um, they only comes where ground's watery an ther's no water, not so much as the tiddliest brook, within no end on a way from yonder. So it ent none o them.'

The scientist pondered seeking for another argument, and the conversation drifted to ghosts in general – the neighbourhood was extremely rich in them. There was the lady in white, who without a head upon her shoulders walked too and fro across a willow bordered bridge. In another direction a ghostly funeral procession wound its way through a country lane to a village churchyard. Many and awsome were the apparitions seen from time to time near the spot where a gibbet once stood. Every big house had its lady in grey, white, or black, and every churchyard a resident ghost of some sort. Everybody knew someone who had seen them if they hadn't actually done so themselves. As generation followed generation each of these ghosts gathered history until a full length novel could have been written about each one of them. Then there were temporary ghosts that were just a nine days wonder, like the one which appeared one winter beside the trunk of one of the beech trees in the avenue outside the gates of the park they had just left; many people saw it with their own eyes, and nothing would induce them to go that way again after dusk. Then the village policeman became active and somehow the ghost melted away. One of the cottages in the hamlet was always supposed to be haunted – the old woman who lived in it for many years declared that many times a woman wearing a striped petticoat came out from the chimney corner, and stood upon one of the flagstones in the centre of the floor – it had a nasty indelible stain upon it.

If they had come down to brass tacks, few, if any, of these country folks really believed their own stories for they were well endued with commonsense – but a pinch of imagination goes a long way towards savouring life. Anyway, it was a rare topic for conversation and had beguiled many a dull half hour in the past, always leaving them with that delightful feeling of excitement.

Gradually the groups grew smaller for the village had already swallowed up nearly half their number, and whenever they came to a cart track branching off from the road one family, at least, turned off towards their lonely farm cottages.

The remaining revellers trudged on towards their distant hamlet – tired and no longer talkative, the children almost, or quite asleep, old ones scarsely capable of putting one foot before the other, were now hanging heavily on kind ones' arms.

Home at last – thank goodness! And there was old Joe Harris's grandfather clock striking twelve! At four next morning some of the men would have to be up and off to the farms to feed the horses and cattle ready for the day's work. Women must be up too, washing, scrubbing, cooking, and scheming to make ends meet. The young gallants to their mouselike corduroys and hobnailed boots in which they would walk patiently up and down, up and down the fields guiding the horses at their work. Docile and obedient to the men – their immediate masters – their hours of kingship over for the present.

The children might lie on for a bit – but not for long for they had a long walk to school. This had been a day of days for them, few of them who are living today have forgotten its thrills. After all most of them were to see one other Jubilee – the silver one of George V.

Tomorrow all must descend to everyday delights. Each to his or her individual battle for life which, no matter how tough it might be, they would wage with grim good humour, never saying die until 'Clerk Tom' was busy with his spade fashioning their last resting place.

'Daidie!' said one as the last 'Good nights' were said – 'If I doon't believe joying yerself baint arder nor work, that I doo!'

'I lay poor old Queen be tired tonight after er gallivanting,' said another 'I do ope they've tucked er up nice an comfortable in bed – Bless er eart.'

Down to earth

It was with reluctance they arose next morning – when their half-crown alarm clocks jerked them rudely into everyday life, it seemed but a few minutes since last night. Soon after sunrise, however, women were downstairs boiling kettles over stick fires and cutting up quarter loaves into thick slices, onto which they scratched a bit of butter, dripping, or lard, sometimes adding a bit of cold bacon or cheese as a relish for their man's midday meal. Flat bottle shaped tin cans were filled with weak tea to wash it down. When this was done, and the coarse brownish white damask cloth spread for breakfast, they opened the stairs door softly and called in a quiet voice 'Joe, Joe' or Tom, Dick, Jack, or Ben as the case might be, and listened for a moment for his answering yawn, and then after latching the door again noiselessly – for the children must not be wakened yet awhile – went on with their work.

Although the 'gay squires' of yesterday were somewhat loth to do so, they hoisted themselves into an upright position, and in an incredibly short time were padding down the crooked stairs in their stockinged feet. They then swilled themselves copiously in the shallow tin pans which were ready filled with rain water and stood on wooden benches just outside the cottage doors. Strange hissings and snorting came from the depths of the tin pans and also from the hard rough towels on which they dried themselves vigorously. Between the friction and the strong yellow soap their faces, when they had finished their ablutions, would be as shining as pieces of lustre ware.

There was never much conversation in the morning when time was at a premium, and today they were more than usually silent, no more than a 'Yes plaze' or 'No thenks' in reply to an offer of replenishment of cup or plate, then a hasty 'Good Marnin' and with a dinner basket slung across their shoulders they went off across the fields to the farm where they worked.

When they got there carter and his boy had already been in the stables an hour or more baiting and watering the horses, giving them a vigorous toilet that made their smooth glossy coats shine like those of seals fresh from the sea. Star, Blossom, Flower, Old Nick, and Snowball came stamping out with their heavy feet like so many wayward school boys, tossing heads to show off manes dressed in numerous little plaits, as carefully as a fine lady's head of hair. They were lovely creatures with well filled frames – no protruding ribs or concave stomachs, for 'those were the days' for beasts as well as men, a good bag of oats was never lacking.

There was a lot of sly fun flying around the farmyard this morning as events were called into mind – jokes about one or another that would stick to them as long as they lived, and are probably still remembered, although the originators have long since turned to dust – it was just as if everything that happened there was recorded on tablets of stone, no one ever forgot anything.

But carter harried them to be quick and hitch to – he was in a hurry to get back to his second breakfast, so the men took each his own horses, fastened their harness and looked them well over to see that all was suent – belly bands neither too tight or too loose, a branch of greenery tucked into headgear to ward off flies, martingale brasses looking bright and all sigarno – the most fastidious would take out his own big red pocket handkerchief and give them an extra rub. Off they went each to the field of his labours, the sound of the iron wheels of the gaily painted blue and orange wagons, on which the farmer's name showed proudly in large lettering, the voices of men calling to horse by name with many 'gee's' or 'wo-o's', or in teasing tones to their boys who led forward, died away in the distance leaving the farm yard with its pleasant combination of smells silently drowsing in the midsummer sunshine until the evening. The only signs of life being the occasional appearance of the old man, kept to dodder about, and the cats that were supposed to keep the mice down – but they were mostly asleep in the sun, while the mice almost jumped over their heads in their swift darting journeys from rick to rick. It was like a scene set for a long ago fairy tale, waiting for the heroine, knight, or ogre to step in.

Hay harvest, which didn't really amount to much hereabouts for it was, and is, corn growing country, was early this year and was now practically finished, only the clearing up to do – one field to get in and the ricks to be made all shipshape and thatched. The men went at it slow and sure as was their wont. There was no use in stampeding for the weather showed no signs of breaking, and the corn harvest wasn't ready yet, although with the wonderful weather of that summer, it showed signs of being so very soon. Then it would be 'hell for leather' with the work, at it from sunrise to dark and sometimes by moonlight, but at the end, their bit of harvest money – that sweetened hard work and no mistake! It was usual to shoe the whole family out of this little windfall, in fact most of the winter wearing apparel was bought with it and then, perhaps, two little piglets to replace the present occupants of the sty, when they were bought indoors to supplement the winter menu. There were not so many kept pigs as there were years ago, owing to the Nuisance Inspector's fussiness. Besides the shopman would always bring a nice piece of bacon with the groceries, some cuts only costing fourpence a pound. Then those little picnic hams for about two shillings were nice and tasty for special occasions such as a feast, weddings, christenings, and funerals, when visitors were certain to turn up. So let who liked keep pigs. Was it worth all the trouble of feeding, mucking them out on Sunday mornings, and putting up with neighbours nasty sayings about the perfume that didn't blend well with that of their Sunday dinners? Some said 'Yes' and some 'No' – but the Sanitary Inspector always had the last word.

It had taken some years to get used to the idea of being interfered with by this man. At first they refused to believe that he had power to make them remove their styes and muckles from where they had been ever since they could remember – if they didn't mind the smell why should he? Anyway, it was a fine healthy smell and anybody who didn't care for it could always pinch their noses when they passed. And who was he pray to come poking about? Their fathers and grandfathers had no such interfering busybody hectoring them about, or the hamlet would never have been there today.

A hundred years ago it had been a wild heath covered with juniper trees when a few tough spirited pioneers had come – from where is not recorded, and settled there. They cut down the juniper trees and with them made foundations for the walls of their dwellings, plastering them within and without with wet mud scooped from the bed of a nearby brook. These primitive dwellings provided at least shelter until they had dug stones enough from the earth to build two roomed cottages – and these are standing yet, wind and weather proof to this day. Only half a dozen or so were added in the years after, built by skilled hands. The cottages stand higgeldy piggeldy, all of a heap to it were, as if the inhabitants were fond of each other's company or feared some danger from the outside world like the stone age men, yet they seemed to crave a little privacy, for most of the cottages turn their backs on each other.

All around them was common land – a few acres were annexed by the settlers who planted root vegetables and sowed a bit of corn which they beat out with a flail and winnowed with a primitive hand worked fan. The goats were imported, a donkey or two, and the irresistible pig to be their friend and stay. By sheer tenacity of purpose they wrested a living from their small kingdom. They had, no doubt, dreams of enlarging their boundaries by bringing under cultivation year by year more of the good ground around them, but their hopes were thwarted by the Lord of the Manor who also, seeing the prospect was good, gathered in all the common land to his already adequate estate.

They were not the kind of men who lie down and die at the first stroke of adversity. They fought tooth and nail against the injustice, taking down fences which were erected to signify ownership – not once but many times, nearly, or quite, landing themselves in prison. But the battle is and always was to the strong, and at that time the rich were all powerful – laws were made to accommodate them, for were they not the law makers?

So there it lies to the present day, a few acres of land surrounding the little group of cottages, hedged in and owned by those who came after the pioneers. They and their sons went forth to work on the surrounding farms, which were then mostly owned by their enemy the Lord of the Manor, no doubt with some bitterness at first, but now that has all been forgotten. Only one man who had managed to annex a bit more land than the others – and little enough at that – remained his own master until the day of his death. He could be seen until almost double with age working on his bit of land often until darkness blotted him from view.

About the ownership of two of the cottages a vendetta raged for many years, it probably began in the second generation, and was still going strong at the time of the Diamond Jubilee. At some time in the past the law had been sought, but although the victor was well pleased to abide by it, the vanquished was anything but willing to do so – and so the war continued. As they lived next to each other, it was very convenient for one to make life very tedious for the other in all sorts of pretty childish ways, that must have given the doer much trouble and inconvenience, one of their little vagaries was to ring a bell every time their enemy was observed to cross his threshold. The ting ting of the bell could constantly be heard all over the hamlet above the buzzing of the bees on flower-scented summer afternoons, and neighbours would smile meaningly at each other as they went in and out of their cottages carrying clothes baskets full of dry linen, or chuckle to themselves without looking up from their gooseberry picking. When they first became conscious of the sound the children of each generation would ask what it meant, but all they could learn was that old Master Adams was in his garden – the feud had lasted so many years that nobody now seemed to know what it was about. Now and then it flared up like a volcano and really desperate deeds were done – such as knocking a hole in the wall of the other's cottage thus exposing the sacred interior to the world at large.

The men in the field worked rather languorously, which was not to be wondered at considering the intense heat, added to the discomfort of stomachs overworked on the previous day. Now and then an eye was cocked towards the road that skirted the fields, for along this the farmer himself would come presently riding in his yellow trap drawn by a glossy coated, well fed cob and driven by one of his two elegant sons. His deputy, the bailiff had been down upon them like a whirlwind almost before they had got into the field scuttling across the hay stubble on his little old strawberry roan, issuing orders this way and that swearing in a voice that sounded like the wind in a hollow. He was a dry husk of a man with a complexion that matched his pony's coat. He grumbled incessantly, and was thoroughly detested.

The farmer himself was a different matter. He had them all 'in the hollow of his hand' owning as he did three of the largest farms in the district. With the exception of one or two, who worked on smaller farms on the other side, and the one or two who were not employed on farms at all, all the men of the hamlet, as well as those of the village, and some yet farther away worked for him. Most of them from boyhood till death. He had taken the place of the of Lord of the Manor in their lives since that family had come to desolation and sold most of the land, which had been acquired by fair means or foul, to fling into the vortex of their debts. It was unthinkable that they should get themselves out of his good books, or what would happen to them and their families? The other farmers employed but few, and there was no other work to be got. At the present there are factories scattered about the district that are well within reach and, no doubt, the boot is on the other foot. It is the farmer who has to walk warily or the workers will fly off like hot fat. Even then there was the beginning of a restless spirit amongst the younger ones, they were no longer content to live and die without seeing anything of the world as their fathers and grandfathers had done – there was a revival of the tough adventurous spirit of their ancestors who had cut down the juniper trees and created their colony out of almost nothing at all. So in the late nineties several of the unmarried men set out for Yorkshire where wages were reported to be much higher. Here they tied themselves to farmers for a year, but at the end of that time, many found that it was not the 'Promised Land' they had hoped to gain, and they migrated to Canada or Australia. They must have found the prospect more pleasing for they stayed there until the first world war called them back to fight for the Motherland. Then they were not backward in coming forward and at the first sound of the bugle they were off from their lonely shacks and farmsteads, leaving all they had behind them to the chance of their return, chafing at delays and formalities which strewed their way back to Europe. Those who were left after the war went back across the seas, for the littleness of life in the village and hamlet, and of the farms, which they had once thought so vast, appalled them in contrast to the freedom of the immense countries of their adoption, and there, except for those who have already drifted into the fair land beyond life, they still are. Their sons and daughters who are far taller and broader and stronger that they were themselves in their youth, and their grandchildren have tied them still closer to these far away countries, not to mention the possessions they have accumulated and which none, but the most incurable idealist, would care to leave. So, no doubt, the hamlet with its strangely assorted inhabitants, the village with its tiny church and schoolhouse, the Squire and his relations, whose vast importance was sliding relent-lessly to the ground, the feud with the new parson, and the near deity of the great farmer from whom they had earned their first few shillings, all of which had played so important a part in their early life, is to them but a vaguely remembered dream, a story to be told, with the faintest of sighs, to their decendants.

But on that hot June day in ninety seven, those long journeys in search of something, which they may or may not have found, had not yet begun. Life's discontent was yet to come. Looking like field mice in their earth coloured suits of corded velveteen with caps thrust back to display thick fringes of fair or mousey hair, delicately tanned with rosy complexions and shining blue eyes – there was not a single pair of dark eyes amongst them. Gentle and pliable both in mind and matter, obedient to the men who were in immediate authority over them, they went to and fro at their work leading the big horses from cock to cock, where the men picked up the hay on their long two-tined forks and tossed it to the man on the wagon. Although the boys were meekness itself to the men, their masters, with the horses they couldn't repress a little swaggering 'Gee up I tell ee, Flower' or 'Goo on, Dumplin, or us shant get round field afoore morning', they would call in such masterful voices – then the young gallants of yesterday were again recognisable.

They were good boys, as boys go, for in those days father usually kept a stick under the table as an antidote to mothers coddling – not that she herself would have spared the rod when it was deserved – 'as the twigs bent so the tree grows' she would tell herself and hit out on the strength of it, 'better a bit of a leatherin now, than a son grown up to be ashamed on.' They had few failures in their bringing up, and people responsible for the bringing up of boys of the present age might do far worse than take a pattern from them.

The farmer came in his shiny trap at ten o'clock when the men were sitting under the hedge eating their bavor and, after all their alertness, they didn't even hear him come for the feet of the staid old cob, and the rubber tyres of the trap made little sound on the soft unmade road. He rarely held any conversation direct with the men for the bailiff was his mouthpiece, and he passed by on the other side without them knowing – which was rather hard on them for they would still have to keep eyes and ears cocked for his coming when they resumed work. This was quite uncalled for, because he very rarely found fault and in every way was anything but a hard master, it was just a matter of form with him to pretend to themselves and each other that he was so fearsome. Although he was endued with so much power, he had never been known to use it other than wisely and justly. The men in their turn knew better than to take advantage, besides, it would never have occurred to them to be late to their work or slipshod in the doing of it – those unpleasant habits were not yet thought of. Fieldwork, their homes and gardens, and a little galli-vanting twice or thrice a year was their life. No wistful longing while they worked for the motor bike waiting to whisk them off to dog racing or suchlike, at towns thirty miles or so away, the moment they had finished, or before if possible.

In stature, as well as metaphorically, the farmer was a giant towering over all other men in the neighbourhood, and in late years he had grown immensely stout, so that now he almost filled the trap, weighting it down on his side and tilting his slim young son precar-iously in the air. He sat in Buddha-like contemplation gazing on his fields to right and left – remote as God himself – it seemed strange that at his own fireside in the midst of his tall and comely daughters, for he had no wife now, he became frankly human – a medley of quips and cranks and queer enduring little ways, just like the rest of mankind. But this view of him was rarely vouchsafed to his humble neighbours, no doubt those of his own castle knew more of him thus.

Snatches of conversation flew over the hedges as they passed by where the men were sitting, followed by a chorus of hearty laughter that had drowned the sound made by the horse and trap. He gave an almost inaudible chuckle at something old Pollitt was saying. 'Bless me!' he said presently, 'I could run to Oxford and back while old Pollitt is drawing out a couple of dozen words.' His son's thoughts were otherwise, no doubt, far above such trivialities – or so thought Youth, for he did not reply or even smile within himself at the very thought of his father accomplishing such a feat – but sat with bright expectant looking eyes, looking steadfastly into the future. What was his dream? And has it, I wonder, come true?

And what were the men laughing so uproariously about? Whatever the joke, it has long since been buried in the past with all the other dead things of fifty-odd years, and if today an echo of it should be heard, it would sound inane and provoke no mirth in this sophisticated generation.

'Av ee eared any moor about that there forchun as is a coming o ee, master Pollitt?' asked a quiet little man, with an amber moustache and twinkling blue eyes.

Mr Pollitt secured the cork in his can by bringing down his fist heavily upon it while he thought deeply upon this question before answering.

'W-a-a-al, J-o-o-e,' he began, stretching out his vowels like a piece of catapult elastic, 'I b-e-a-n-t- a-s-s-u-r-e-d o n-o-t-h-i-n, t-h-a-a-t I b-e-a-n-t.'

'Come now,' said one of the others, 'you doon't mean to say us be gooing to be done out on the treating you promised so faithful?'

'Every man Jack on ee shall get someat – if I gets it,' promised the old man. 'But now it seems there baint no proof on my grampy ever aving bin born – they thinks I ought to known wher ee wur christened.'

'Wa-al! That's a rum un if you like,' opined the others and began to discuss the matter amongst themselves. It appears that a short time previously a man of shabby genteel appearance had come to the village in quest of someone of the name of Pollitt and being directed by a woman – who was simply bursting to know what business the stranger was upon – so found himself at the doorway of the out of the way cottage that housed old Pollitt and his wife: they were old and their large family had all married long ago.

The man produced a card at the same time, which was just as well because Mrs Pollitt could not focus her old sight on the small print even with the help of her steel-rimmed spectacles, told her that he was a lawyer and that he had come to see her husband – relating to a large fortune that was awaiting him.

If Mrs Pollitt said, and she almost certainly did, when confiding the story to her friends, that so slight a thing as a feather would have floored her, she was by no means overstating her feelings, in fact she had to cling to the door in order to keep her balance. When she had somewhat recovered herself her visitor was already seated on the old horsehair sofa, a cup of tea in his hand and a slice of dough cake, left over from Sunday, balanced on his knee. She had produced these automatically, for any stranger who entered any cottage thereabouts was instantly invited to a cup of tea – they all knew what was what where hospitality was concerned.

In the meantime a boy from the next-door cottage had been dispatched to the field where Master Pollitt was at work with a curt message to tell him to come home instanter. Until he came no details could be discussed. The man seemed to enjoy his tea – he had had a long walk and it was a warm day. Mrs Pollitt couldn't help noticing that his clothes (real gentleman's clothes) were by no means new. The starched cuffs of his shirt were slightly frayed and neither they, nor the Gladstone collar, were quite spotless – she noticed this particularly because she had been used to taking in a bit of washing from one of the big houses so knew how gentlemen's linen should look. It was strange that she should be able to dwell on such insignificant things while such momentous events were pending. 'I think I must have been a bit light headed,' she declared afterwards.

Soon the clank clank of nailed boots on the flagstones without announced old Pollitt, full of consternation for it was unheard of for a man to be called out of the fields except in the direst extremity – no hint had been given in the message as to the unique happenings which were now afoot. When he found his wife alive and well, his home not lying in ruins, and the pig, which he had, at least, feared to have been taken sick and dying before its time, hale and healthy, he was relieved but bewildered. His bewilderment increased when the visitor jumped up from the sofa and taking his hand in a friendly grasp congratulated him upon his good fortune. Old Pollitt sank into the nearest chair and mopped the sweat from his brow. He wondered if he was going off his head.

The lawyer came to the point at once, taking out a note book, he began to ask the old man a few questions about his ancestry, carefully writing down the answers, with which he seemed very satisfied. 'The long and short of it is, Mr Pollitt, that there is a nice little fortune – I don't say a large one, but a nice little windfall that I'm sure you will find most acceptable, waiting for you in the Chancery. A brother of your grandfather's who went to Australia many years ago and died there about the time you were born, yes nearly seventy years ago. He made money there, but as he never married, he had no direct heir, and when he died, as no relative came forward to claim it his money went to the state, to be taken care of until such a time as the heir, whoever he might be, should ask for it – '

'What?' broke in Mrs Pollitt angrily. 'When all the while us wer hard put to find bread to put in our chuldern's mouths. What business has them Chancey folks to keep it if it belonged to us?'

'Our chuldern never went hungry, Mother,' said the old man placatingly. 'Us allys found someat for um, that us did. Not like when I wer a youngster, then us did know what it was to ave nowt but wind in our bellies. It wus all barley bread – as black as pitch and nowher near enough on it. A-h-h! Us wer glad enough to pull a turnup out on a field and gobble that, that us wer.'

'Those were the hungry forties indeed,' said the lawyer. 'The law too was hard on the poor in those days – to take an almost worthless thing like a turnip was considered a crime to be punished by banishment or even the gallows.'

'Not in this shire, Mister, no farmer hereabouts ever begrudged a ungry child one on his turnips. T'wer poor feed though.'

'But let us get back to our business,' suggested the lawyer, as he glanced at the clock, with scarlet geraniums painted upon the lower half of its glass front, which stood on the high mantelpiece. 'You can depend upon me to do all that is necessary – there are certificates of births and deaths needed. I have already looked into several parish registers and found most of the entries, all will be plain sailing when we have these.'

More conversation ensued in which politic reference was made to payment of the lawyer's professional services – for, of course the kind gentleman wasn't altogether a philanthropist. It was most necessary that the case should be in the hands of a skilled lawyer – one who had all the strange and mysterious ways of these Chancery people at his finger tips. Ten per cent of the total of the heritage would not be at all outrageous – this was explained to the old people who gladly agreed, for wouldn't it be wonderful to get anything when less than an hour ago they had expected nothing at all, and the workman was worthy of his hire? So a paper was put before them to sign and the woman next door called in to witness it. She, by the way, took the visitor to be one of those insurance agents that had lately been about teasing the life out of everybody to join their societies. Before night-fall it was all over the hamlet that the Pollitts had fallen victims and had actually signed – one of them must be suffering from some secret illness and expecting to die ere long.

If the skies had opened and rained down golden sovereigns upon them the old couple could have not been more astonished than at the happenings of the afternoon. For a week or two they walked on air – in imagination Mrs Pollitt squandered money with abandon, such as only those with nothing to spend can do. Strangely enough, for in her lifetime she had longed wistfully for all sorts of things, she thought of nothing for herself now. Her children too, who in her earlier years had been of such vital importance, had by now receded from her, the homes of their husbands and wives were their homes, theirs the advice given and taken, not hers, their loves were centred in their own families – it was nature's decree, just as she herself had imperceptibly drifted from her parents, so had they. They had become just, very likeable, other men and women now. There was still love between them but it was of a different kind to that of earlier times. The children were not lacking in dutiful kindness for the old folks – but it was mixed with a very visible impatience.

But the grandchildren! Ah! The grandchildren were a different matter. They were the core of her life now as their parents had once been. Theirs were the paths Grannie Pollitt longed to pave with gold. At least, her dreams were full of velvet suits, tin trumpets, embroidered frocks, sweets and sugar covered biscuits without stint.

She herself was not so badly put to as she had been in earlier years, wages were better and only herself and the old man to keep – in fact she had quite a little hoard of five shilling pieces and half crowns put away in the metal teapot on the shelf ready for dire emergencies. But what about the several old folks in the hamlet who had nothing but their beggarly half crown a week from the parish? She would help them by stealth, half pounds of tea, screws of sugar, pats of fresh butter, and other necessities would find their way to their cupboards regularly. And she wouldn't forget those who were not quite so needful but had been kind friends to her either. She would be a Lady Bountiful – the pleasantest of all dreams to those who are themselves poor.

They decided at first to tell nobody. Then several letters came for them by post, addresses in a handwriting that even the postman couldn't place, try as he might. What too was strange, he thought, was that Mrs Pollitt took them without a word beyond 'Thank ee, Postman.' His clients were in the habit of saying when he handed them a letter, 'Oh, that's from our Liz – she wants someat, I know,' or 'Whatever's me Aunt Soph writing for? I bet she's a comin a Sunday now,' or else 'Ah-h! Our young Ame – feels a bit mother sick, I low, her fust time away and all.' They often opened the letter and read little bits to him, or if their sight was bad, or they couldn't read at all – being no scholards, as they said – he would read it through to them while he drank a cup of tea or a glass of homemade wine to fortify himself for the rest of his journey. But Mrs Pollitt's silence mystified him completely.

Then it all came out somehow. From that moment everybody was on tenterhooks. Married daughters from not too far distant farm cottages and villages were, more than usually, frequent visitors. Sons, either of their own accord, or prompted by their wives, came over regularly on Sunday mornings to do a few chores for the old people – and incidently to 'learn the lay of the land'. Things were going on like a house on fire.

But presently a state of stalemate was proclaimed. One birth or baptism certificate was not to be found – it may have been a case of illegitimacy far back in the past, or records of some village church may have been lost or destroyed. Whatever the cause it brought matters to a complete standstill and so the Pollitts' fortune still lies in Chancery. They were in no wise cast down for as Mrs Pollitt replied to all her sympathisers, 'What you never has you never misses.' As a sop to her disappointment, if such existed, she took one of the wagon wheels – as five shilling pieces were called – from her teapot and spent it riotously on her grandchildren.

The one to be most bitterly disappointed at the breakdown of negotiations was the lawyer who had set them afoot. Of course he was a man of little repute, some act at the beginning of his career having resulted in a term of imprisonment and his name being struck off the rolls. Sadder and wiser, no doubt, after his release he had managed to make a precarious living by any law work which offered – his advice was expert, and as long as he kept himself in the back-ground, all was well. His scheme of tracing the relatives of those whose estates were locked up in Chancery had proved quite lucrative, for he had several successes. He had been almost certain that the Pollitts' case was as good as won when he first called upon them. Whatever his past may have been he was perfectly honest with them.

As to old Master Pollitt – he didn't turn a hair when his wife read out the letter containing the final verdict to him. He hadn't thought of a thing to spend it on, apart from a few pints of fourpenny for his fellow workers. Riches, like everything else, are only by comparison. And there he was at that moment with his evening meal before him – a magnificent slice of home cured ham, the frying of which had perfumed half the hamlet, and an immense basin of his best Magnum potatoes, with a currant roly-poly to follow: having been reared on barley bread and raw turnips, wasn't that riches enough?

The roadman

Sam the roadman went in the opposite direction to the others, up the gorse-edged gravelled lane towards the turnpike: a long straight white road which began with the loveliest of cities and ended in plain South Midlands towns, it was built of hard flinty-looking stones and pyramids of these were heaped at intervals along the grass verge. Sam had spent most of his life breaking these and pounding them soundly into pot holes that were constantly appearing along the road. Despite the apparent hardness of the stones in dry weather, the road threw off a cloud of white dust, much to the discomfort of those who travelled along it, especially pedestrians who were apt to appear at their destination with boots and clothes covered looking for all the world, as it was said, like miller's assistants. This was most provoking, especially when their mission was a funeral and their decent black was turned willy nilly into a costume more becoming a wedding guest.

Otherwise it was a pleasant road high up and looking down upon cornfields and snatches of woodland – on either side the wide grass verge sloped downwards to the hedgerow which was crowned with wild roses, honeysuckle, traveller's joy and a variety of wild berries, each in their season. The verges too were scattered with flowers – cowslips, moondaisies, ladies' gloves, patches of yarrow and many other suchlike common flowers and herbs that thrive in those parts, with here and there a few Scots bluebells – these were always noticed with pleasure by country folk in passing, as was the heavenly blue of the speedwell's starry flowers, which must have cheered and encouraged many who passed along the narrow path. The path had been trodden by generations of footsteps near to the hedge, which gave comforting protection from wind, sun and rain, and provided shadow for the fugitive – for many such must have passed that way in the course of time – and a pleasant remoteness for those who wished to talk secretly or to withdraw into themselves.

Sam was none of these, he craved neither secrecy nor remoteness – his mind, naive and gay, was an open book that all who ran might read. He delighted to engage in conversation with any who had wish or leisure to pause – and with still greater pleasure did he retail any scraps of information he thus gathered to his friends and neighbours of the hamlet later – so did he form a vital artery between his world and the large world beyond. Although most of the people of the hamlet now took at least one newspaper a week, they were a bit wary about swallowing their contents whole – such glibness was best taken with more than a grain of salt – the most candid critics among them declared that they were just a pack of lies from beginning to end. But Sam's news by word of mouth, even the most fantastic reports, were always acceptable. Anyway, it usually outran the newspapers by a day or two, and when they were on rare occasions worked up to burning anxiety about a case, as they were about the trial of Mrs Dyer the baby farmer, Sam was welcomed as a hero when he brought the verdict given to him by a passer-by. Guilty! Some spoke of lighting a bonfire.

He had with others of his little community felt a bit slothful on this particular morning, and when he had started out it had already gone six by the hooter – a pale ghost of a sound, subject to the whimsies of the wind, which came from the brewery several miles distant. By it all the dwellers in the surrounding countryside set their clocks.

Polly had called him as usual, but because of the muzziness of his head he had not hurried. 'Come on Sam,' she had called a second time. 'T'is no use you favouring lurking, holiday is over – its workaday today.' There were no children in their house to awake betimes. She poured the boiling water from the kettle into the big black teapot and set it on the hob to brew, then paused to take an ample pinch of snuff.

Sam yawned loudly as he slumped into the Windsor armchair which was the throne of the man of the house – it was a poor home indeed that hadn't an armchair for its master; where such was missing or employed by herself, the missis was certainly not quite up to scratch. The thick slice of bacon sizzling in the pan over the wood fire smelt enticing; as Sam drank down his basin-sized cup of sweet hot milkless tea, he began to feel that life was pleasant after all, the top-like spinning in his head had stopped after a good swill in cold water on the form outside beneath the lilac tree.

When Polly had placed his slice of bacon on the plate before him and replenished his cup, she sat herself down dolefully by the hearth and continued to take her snuff. A bird couldn't have lived on the food she consumed – she seemed to live entirely on snuff, by now she was almost mummified by it. It was sprinkled on the bodice of her olive green dress and on the beaded apron that covered her time-worn skirt. The creases in her plain face were full of it. She was a little roly-poly of a woman – the shape of a cottage loaf, her nondescript hair drawn back tightly into a farthing bun at the back of her little round head. She was twenty years older than Sam who was now about forty-five – they were a strangely assorted couple. Neighbours who still remembered her coming to the village talked quietly to each other to this day of the mystery that had surrounded her, and which they had never been able to probe for she kept her own counsel except on one subject and that only to the one woman she had made her friend – that was the story of her rich Aunt Bucket.

That Aunt Bucket had actually lived, and that she was a woman of taste and refinement, was apparent in the relics that Polly still possessed. She spoke to her friend of beautiful double damask table-cloths of yards and yards in length and breadth lying at the bottom of her box upstairs. She brought out handsome shawls of fine and elegant texture from the chest of drawers downstairs, one of these of cream cashmere of immense dimensions she insisted on lending for the christening of every one of her friend's babies so that it was known in that family as 'The Christening shawl'. As a delicate way of announcing the advent of yet another infant, the mother was apt to say in a jocular way, 'I hope the moth hasn't got into the Christening shawl, Mrs Trimble, for I shall have to be giving it another airing after a bit!' The shawl was bequeathed upon one of them at Polly's death. It had probably been worn as a wedding shawl over a crinoline dress by a pretty young woman many years before.

Then, arranged on the case of stuffed owls that stood on the sidetable just within the cottage door, were wine glasses with twisted stems, a cut glass jug and salt cellars, while on the chest of drawers and high mantelpiece – all mixed up with such crude ornaments as 'Morning and Evening Exercises' 'The Last into Bed puts out the Light' in which little chamber pots with gilt linings were prominent – were several pieces of Dresden and Royal Worcester, and some cups and saucers of Crown Derby, a pair of Chelsea figures and a beautifully inlaid teatray. All these things must have once belonged to a person of affluence and good taste, yet there was not a glimmer of these qualities in the child of her adoption – for she had been not only aunt but mother to Polly. How came she to be in such low estate temporally and spiritually? It was a long story told bit by bit to her friend under a vow of secrecy – neither of them taking into consideration the little child who sat on a low stool taking it all in.

When Sam had been a strapping young man of twenty, his father, old Sam, a widower of several years standing, had brought Polly from nobody knew where (wild guesses were made by all and sundry) as housekeeper for the two of them – with view to marriage with himself, at least that's how the story ran. But when the term of her probation was ended and the simple preparations for the wedding made, it caused a great sensation in the hamlet when lo and behold!, young Sam went forth as bridegroom to the middle aged and somewhat unattractive bride. And never a word of the whys and wherefores had been given out from that day to this. However, the three of them lived a seemingly happy trio until in the natural course of events old Sam was carried off in a farm wagon to the churchyard.

'My head's splittin,' moaned Polly now.

Sam grunted on a kind note as he hewed himself another slice from the loaf to dip in the bacon fat and poured himself another cup of tea – this gesture being in acknowledgement of Polly's indisposition, for in those days a man never lifted a finger to wait upon himself at table unless it were in times of stress and illness of his partner, and then it was self-consciously, with a clumsy fist and a rather ashamed feeling that he was doing 'woman's work', regarded by others as a poor injured innocent. There was a distinct line drawn between the work of men and women – one young man who had been a soldier, and thus become accustomed to making himself handy, was spoken of by his neighbours with much ridicule because he helped his wife to scrub the floors, mangle the clothes and, at a push, wash the children.

But now the vague sound of the hooter came through the open doorway and therefore he must be off or that dratted road surveyor would be on the spot before him – it was just like him to be peeking about this morning, hoping to catch him late after the holiday. So hastily tying the laces of his stout well-dubbined boots, and fastening the black leather straps which he wore just below the knees over his dust-coloured corduroys, he donned his shapeless felt hat, threw his dinner basket across his shoulders, and grasping the stout ash stick from the corner by the door he hurried forth.

As he passed the sty the pig came out and gave a fanfare of delighted little squeals and grunts. 'I can't stop to feed you this morning, Jack,' he began apologetically. 'Missis ull give e yer breakfast' – but there, how could he resist such a joyful welcome? 'There my pretty, there be a bit of relish for ee,' throwing a bunch of sowthistle that had been growing nearby. 'Good Jack! Good pig!' – he was that, although folks always said 'them sandy ones never throve'.

He filled his short clay pipe with its negress head bowl as he walked along the gravelled lane with its deep ruts. Not many of his fellow hamleteers could afford more than one pipe a day, and that in the evening when their work was done, but as well as having no family to bring up, and Polly no doubt having brought a bit in her stocking, Sam's wages were more than those of the men who worked in the fields, sixteen shillings a week to their fourteen, so he could well afford to indulge in an extra pipe, especially on such a morning as this.

Larks were singing as they soared into the sky above the field beyond the hedge, and the gorse bushes by the wayside were alive with birdsong. He looked into the sky knowingly as he hummed a few notes of 'Ta ra ra Bumdeay'. 'Another hot day today,' he thought to himself: the larks were rising straight up, and at the least sight of rain, they went up by fits and starts, then dropped like stones. This morning they soared almost out of sight into the blue sky and returned as effortlessly as thistledown on the wind.

The furious ringing of a bicycle bell caused Sam to sidestep hastily onto the grass verge. 'Another of them steel horses! Dangerous contraptions! A man's life was in jeopardy every time he went abroad,' he began to grumble to himself, jolted for the moment out of his man-of-the-world attitude towards these modern nuisances. Besides, when the rider came abreast of him, and proved to be one for whom he had particular regards, his mind broadened considerably towards steel horses in general and this one in particular.

'Good morning, Robert,' he called out amiably. Now here was a man for you if ever there was one. Although a stonemason by trade, he was a regular politician. Could tell you the goings on of them 'igh up uns' in the Liberal Party word for word. And what them rank old Tories were up to as well. Sam took a delight in politics (as he saw them, and Robert related them). Although he couldn't read a word he took a newspaper with decided Liberal views which Polly read to him in her toneless voice, and when there was anything particularly striking he would often take it round to Robert's home that he might read it through to him a second time to make sure that Polly had made no mistake. Then Robert would air his own opinions to this faithful disciple, greatly to Sam's admiration. Every word was Gospel truth to him, never a moment would he have believed that political talk is ninety nine per cent clap trap. With singleness of heart he loved the Liberals, and hated the Tories. Like Dr Fell's enemy he didn't know exactly why – but so it was he asserted himself, and none of the farm men could do that, for if they didn't vote as their Gaffer did, they had to pretend to be in his boat.

The stonemason returned Sam's greeting with gravity. He was a serious man in the early forties with grave dark eyes and a fair complexion. He was something of a solitary having little in common with his neighbours – this was partly because he had been town bred (in a small country town it is true) and of fairly well-to-do parentage, and had thus acquired different tastes in his youth. He had come into the district a very young man, had married hastily before he was old enough for marriage and had felt marooned ever since. Sometimes, after the children had gone to bed, he wrote his bits of poetry, but they were laboured and immature specimens and when he read them out, his wife always said they sounded silly and discouraged him. She liked people to have common sense and practicality – like herself, and thought bitterly he would be much better employed mending the children's shoes.

But there was no time for serious talk this morning; the cyclist was soon half a mile ahead of the plodding pedestrian who, come what might, couldn't help pausing now and then to watch anything that caught his fancy. However, he at last arrived at the point where he left off work yesterday, and drawing the long handled hammer from under the heap of stones where he had hidden it, and donning the black spectacles to protect his eyes from splinters, he was soon industriously breaking the large flinty blocks into tiny pieces.

He had been working for less than half an hour when he heard, between the beats of his hammer, footsteps approaching and paused to listen. A heavy tread, neither fast – wearing out its pace before the journey was scarce begun, as one not used to walking usually did – nor yet slow – dawdling away the time. The step of someone used to covering long distances, and although heavy it had a hollow sound – betokening boots the worse for wear. Before Sam took off his black spectacles, the better to see who came, he had judged it to be a regular roadster such as passed by very often. 'Good Marnin to ye,' he said good humouredly – for all men were his brothers.

'Good Marnin, Mister,' replied the tramp – a gloomy scarecrow of a fellow. His clothes scarcely held together – he looked half starved too, but what went to Sam's kind heart most was the sight of a dirty big toe poking through one of his battered boots. The man paused for a moment adding Sam up, then said hungrily, 'Spose you ent got a bit o bread you don't want, Mister?'

Sam hesitated – if he gave away his bit of bavor he would have to go without himself till dinnertime, and it was a long time to twelve o' clock – breaking stones on an empty stomach was no joke, and the hearty breakfast of bread and bacon had been forgotten. Still the poor chap was hungry, one could almost see through him he was that thin. Sam picked up his dinner basket and the man's face brightened, without a word Sam handed him a thick slice of bread and dripping – that left one for himself: after all Polly, thinking to let him down lightly after yesterday's feasting, had put in an extra one today.

Taking stock of Sam's softness the man dared further. 'I spose you ent got a drop of cold tea? I could jest about do we a drink,' he whined. 'Walked all the way from Brum I ave, and scarce a bit or drop inside me all the way an thats the honest truth, Mister, I'll et me at if it ent.'

'That ud be a bit tough,' opined Sam, his gaze resting on the tattered bit of headgear in question. 'I only got erb beer,' he said, producing a tin can from his basket. 'You can have a swig o that if you've a mind to.'

'I don't care what it is as long as it's wet, me throttle's as dry as I don't know what. I got a tin cup if you'll pour me out a drop.' He ate and drank ravenously.

'Walked from Brumegum – that's a goodish step,' mused Sam, who was feeling pleased and goodish with himself for his good deed. 'A underd miles or as near as no odds I'll be bound.'

'Moor like six underd when you comes to walk it – not that I ent walked longer stretches o the road. Not a bad game nither – when you've got something in yer belly and a pair o good soles to yer feet.' He looked enviously at his benefactor's stout hobnails.

Sam put on the black glasses, which shut in his good nature like a curtain. The chap would be wanting to swap shoes next. 'I must be getting on befoor my gaffer comes along,' he said cheerfully, by way of breaking up the conversation. 'Good day to'y,' he added as the other ambled off.

Presently came along a stout middle-aged woman perched precariously on a bicycle, the wife of a prosperous tradesman in the not far distant town who had, she always explained to everyone with whom she conversed, taken up cycling on her doctor's orders – for just then it was a popular means for weight reduction. Not many women of her age and size had yet taken up this fashionable exercise, and she was generally supposed to look rather foolish, but she persevered heroically. So intent was she now upon her front wheel, that she didn't notice Sam until she came a cropper almost on top of his heap of stones.

'No bones broke I hopes, Maam?' he asked kindly, as he helped her to sort herself and her machine out. She was confused and shaken but nothing worse. 'I should sit meself down here on the grass for a bit if I wus yu Maam.'

'Oh no! I'm quite alright – it was very silly of me!' declared the lady, at the same time feeling she'd like nothing better than to sit down here and now, until she recovered her equilibrium – but no, she could not bear to put herself in such a ridiculous position. Supposing anyone who knew her should come along, as well they might, and see her sitting beside the roadman on the edge of the highway. A thousand times no, she would rather die in the attempt to remount her cycle – and she had never really overcome that difficult feat, although she could go along like a ship in full sail when once mounted. So pushing the bicycle a little way on, she made a gallant attempt but floundered. Watching with great interest Sam let her have another and yet another try, then throwing down his hammer, he scurried after her. 'If yu like, Maam, I'll give e a bump up,' and without waiting upon further ceremony he grabbed the cycle and held it firmly until the lady had found her balance.

'Them there folks,' he ruminated as he watched her out of sight, 'as av got a bit o money think themselves everybody, but when it comes to a bit of a fall they ent nobody, that they bent.' Just what he meant he wasn't quite sure himself.

Two horses came trotting along the greensward, high stepping, handsome creatures. These riders too did not see Sam because they were too intent on each other to see anything else in the visible world. The fair young girl who was wearing a sombre black habit against which her hair showed burnished and gleaming, was sitting side saddle upon her lovely chestnut, her soft blue eyes were turned towards the brown ones of her companion as she listened enraptured to his animated conversation – he dark, handsome, debonair – a very lord of creation.

'Owns th world,' thought Sam as they passed. 'That they do.'

The carrier's cart from a neighbouring village came jogging along filled with women going to the little market town to do their shopping. The tailboard was laden with oil cans and an empty beer barrel. The carrier cracked a joke with Sam as they passed, and one of the women squealed out, 'How's old Mrs Binger, Sam? I heared she was middlin bad.'

'Oh she's still feathering the foam,' replied Sam. 'Wunt die while she can see anybody else alive, I lay.'

'Did e see our young Lord Summerby come riding along a bit agog we is lady love?' called another of the women. 'Now there will be a fine igh falooting weddin before long I'll be bound.' The gentry had funny ways – no sooner plighted than wed – instead of walking out with each other for two or three or maybe five or six years as the village youths and maids did, very cautious like, which gave them a chance to know the worst about each other and to decide if they could put up with it for life.

The cart jogged on its way, the women under the tilt chattering like a nest of magpies – here was a topic that never failed to set them all agog for they dearly loved a bit of romance.

The morning was getting up. 'Ten o'clock,' mused Sam as he looked up to see how far the sun had travelled. Taking up his basket he retired to the shade of the hedge where, sitting with his feet in the ditch, he ate his bavor – if you've never eaten bread and dripping with your feet in a ditch, try it now and you'll agree that it is more excellent than a royal banquet and a throne.

A quick light trotting of hooves in the near distance just as he was taking his last swallow of the herb beer made him get up and hurry to the roadside, his eyes glistening with pleasure – here was a well-known equipage from his own hamlet. A high spirited little donkey drawing a miniature dogcart and driven by one as spirited as himself – that was easy to see by the way he was going. For some folks he would jib and sulk and behave like a naughty child, so that they thought he was not worth the ninepence charged for his hire, and preferred to walk and carry their heavy parcels themselves: although it may seem like a fairy tale in these days of scarcity, parcels of groceries, even those of the poorest families, were very heavy. For instance twelve pounds of sugar was but one of the usual weekly items where there was a family of a round dozen to provide for. Fortunately food was plentiful and cheap, thus accommodating itself to their incomes and numbers.

Sam glanced admiringly at the approaching cavalcade. Neddy, in whom all the hamleteers took a proprietary interest, came flying onward like an Arab steed, he was on his mettle feeling the purposeful hand upon his rein. His driver, a woman in the middle forties, with intelligence written all over her, was as smart as a new pin in a moss green coat and skirt – shabby it is true, for it had seen many a day's wear as had the chip straw hat with its bunch of rosebuds neatly planted in the front and which was worn four square on her head. Yes, she must remember to get a pennyworth of gum arabic at the chemist's while she was in town today to freshen it up again, her little daughter's best hats needed touching up too, so it wouldn't be like buying something for herself alone. Never was there such a woman for making poverty sit like a red saddle on a white horse.

An avalance of wants always hung over her household of growing children. If it wasn't shoes to be bought or mended then it was a half dozen yards of calico to be turned into under clothing or pieces of blue or pink print to be picked up cheaply, to make the little girls overalls; as to the little boy's knickers they were a perpetual want, sometimes after sitting for hours over them she sometimes threatened to have a pair made for him by the blacksmith of cast iron. So no wonder that out of her infinitesimal income she could almost never afford anything for herself, yet in some miraculous way she always managed to look neat and smart. She was always engaged in making something old into something at least wearable, and the transformation was truly astounding. Apart from the black which she kept for church going, she had only the green costume for going out in, and it was now about three years since the rare day she had been able to send a 10/6 postal order to Mr John Noble of Manchester for one of his celebrated costumes at that price. She had awaited its arrival with pleasurable excitement not unmixed with trepidation, and when it turned out to be a miracle of worth that the better part of ten guineas would not buy at the present day she was pleased, as she many times afterwards told her daughters, as if she had been given a golden crown. Even now when it had seen its best days, it was a much cherished possession.

She sat bolt upright on the seat, her little boy – brought for the dual purposes of keeping him out of mischief during her absence, and to hold the donkey while she went into the shops – beside her.

'Here's a ooman to be proud on,' thought Sam as he advanced to the edge of the verge. 'Looks like a Duchess set up there that she do – that spic and span, just like her house and children – how she does it caps my dolly that it do, for I'll stake me life that most times tuppence apenny udn't drop out of her purse if it was turned bottom upards – I fear Roberts main reckless we money.'

As they drew parallel with him, Sam waved his arms frantically in front of the donkey; failing thus to halt him he grabbed the rein – much to Neddy's indignation. Sam drew twopence from the depths of his pocket. 'Will e bring me half ounce o bacca, Missis?' he asked. 'There's the apence for it. You can ave the apenny change, me nibbs,' addressing the little white haired boy who grinned from ear to ear at this sudden slice of luck, for halfpennies were few and far between in those days. 'You buy some poppies we it – and mind you takes some on um back for yer sisters – I ates a greedy boy that I do. Black Shag I likes, Missis, its three apence for alf a ounce. You wunt mind, ull you?'

'Not a bit, Sam, only too pleased I assure you. Now hold still there Ned while I put this twopence in my purse. Don't feel very work brittle today do you, Sam, after yesterday's goings on?'

'You never spoke truer. If I were a king I udn't do a stroke today that I udn't. I udn't as it is if that Surveyor chap wusn't liable to come bouncing along any minute.'

'Oh, I expect he feels much the same as you do. Probably he went up to London to see the goings on up there and enjoy himself – if so he won't be in any hurry to come and see what you're up to today, depend upon it.'

'I adn't thought on that,' said Sam, looking delighted at the idea. 'I spose that sort of coves ave got some way o enjoying their selves, though it don't seem feasible.'

But Mrs Roberts had neither time nor inclination for further conversation, she flicked the whip briskly and Neddy who had been straining at the leash took the hint with great gusto.

Now that the morning was well advanced and there was a perfect stream of traffic, scarcely ten minutes passed without some kind of vehicle, either a farmer in his light trap, bound for the nearby market town, a local nobility in smart turnout on business or pleasure bent, or the grocer's spring cart laden with brown paper-covered parcels for customers in distant villages.

Now it was Doctor's gig – but something wrong about it surely? Old Doctor in his patriarchal white beard which had been wont to glow in the distance, his tall hat and other decorous garments, sat in it no longer, vanished too was his equally ancient coachman with his cockaded hat, tight white breeches and blue coat decorated with brass buttons. Only last week they had seemed as concrete as the earth on which Sam stood, for had they not been passing to and fro ever since he had, at the age of ten, broken his first stone? Now their places were usurped by a young man, clean shaven – or at most a military moustache, like any ordinary man – wearing a dark lounge suit and bowler hat. Driving himself too! All the dignity of white beard, silk hat, cockade, indeed all Doctorliness gone. And who would put any faith in a young chap like this, dressed no different to any other man in his Sunday clothes – Sam had a dark suit and bowler hat himself, which he always wore in his capacity of bearer at funerals. Of course Old Doctor had put it about that this young nephew was wonderful clever – so the account came from the college or wherever it was where doctors learnt their business, and now he had learnt all there was to learn seemingly and had come to take over the practice so that Old Doctor could sit back – but folks wouldn't like it! They did not, and Young Doctor was regarded as an usurper for the next twenty years.

The gig drew up. 'Good morning, Roadman,' called the doctor. 'Can you direct me to where old Mrs Gates lives, please?'

'Old Sally Gates,' pondered Sam, thinking, 'Old Doctor udn't ave axed such a question, he knowed the whereabouts of everybody even if they ad moved from where they did live to where they lived now.' 'Wal, she did live in the next house to me when the old man wer alive, but after that she went to live with er daughter Amy at the Pump – but Tom and her didn't hit it off somehow so she moved over to Weston to Fred's – I heard she left there though and I doon't wonder nither for Fred's wife be a bit o a tegremont, I udn't live with er for nowt, that I udn't.'

'Yes, yes,' said the doctor in a slightly impatient voice, 'but where does she live now?'

'I doon't rightly know and that's the solid truth. She must be middlin bad where ever she is – most likely dead by now.'

'What makes you think so?' quizzed the doctor.

'Wal – nobody, cept the gentry, send for doctor till they be sure a body be a going to die for certain – then they sends because they doon't want none o them inquests – nasty things they be.'

'I quite agree,' said the doctor, 'and if you could only call to mind where this wanderer's tent is pitched at the moment, I would hasten there to sign the death certificate and thus avoid the embarrassment.'

Sam pushed back his hat and scratched his head – a sure sign of deep cogitation.

'Hold hard!' he said presently. 'Hold hard! She did, that she did! Went to her daughter Rose's at Pimlico. You just keep on past the second milestone and goo down next turning – a bit of a rough road, you comes to farm house and beyond that is the two cottages where shepherd and carter lives, Jim and Rose lives in one on um but I can't rightly say which.'

'Thank you and Good morning, Roadman.' The gig moved off at a good pace.

Small low voices and mysterious rustlings on the other side of the hedge were the next interruption. Sam crept down to the spot from whence it came and landed a heavy blow with his ash stick on the hedge – sudden silence from beyond.

'Now come you out and let me see who you be,' called Sam, 'or I'll come in there to ee, and give ee a darned good hidin apiece: that u'll larn ee, me young squires, not to goo pullin them bird's nests to bits. Now come on, here's the gate.' Sam had already arrived there for it was only a few yards away, and was regarding three red faced boys with mighty indignation. One had something in his cap which he quickly thrust behind him but he was not smart enough to deceive Sam who demanded to see what he had there, and when he found it was a little frightened bullfinch he promptly confiscated it. The small boy opened his mouth and roared lustily at the loss of his prize. 'I wusn't going to hurt im, I wus only going to put im in a cage and larn im to sing,' he sobbed.

'Ee doon't want none o yure larning,' said Sam. 'If I ent a good mind to put you in a cage and let in larn you, and that I'll do if I catches you agen – now off you goos.'

The boys needed no second bidding, they fled to the other side of the field out of sight and earshot where they promptly began to look for other birds' nests – that being the only kind of mischief that presented itself to their itching fingers.

Sam set the bullfinch free, then settled down to work in real earnest, not even pausing for more than a moment when a scissor grinder and his lady come past quarrelling like a pair of wild cats, or to more than glance when a stray cyclist hailed him. But now, 'What was this a doing?' A young hobble de hoy came hurrying along the road, talking to himself in a high falsetto voice. Sam recognised him as 'Poor Joe' who worked for Farmer Hunt, and was a bit soft in his head. He greeted him with his usual friendliness but Joe looked neither to right or left but shuffled onwards chanting as he went, 'I be a gooing to Muster Ameses to buy a shovel for alf a crown, I be gooing to Muster Ameses to buy a shovel for alf a crown, I be a gooing…' Sam chuckled loudly, 'Whatever be ee up to now?'

Half an hour later the poor lad returned looking very crestfallen and worried, no longer chanting the song of the shovel.

'Well Joe' greeted Sam 'you be soon a gooing back. What ever's appened to ee?'

'I've forgot,' wailed Joe, 'I've forgot! I see'd some'at white down by Ladybridge and I thought it wer the ghost – I wer terrible frit and then I forgot what it wus I'd got to say. Gaffer said I wer to say it out loud all the way so's I shouldn't forget what I wus a gooing for – he'll be that savage. I doon't know what I shall do – I've a good mind to howl.'

'Well doon't ee cry, me lad,' cheered Sam. 'I can tell ee what it wer you wus a gooing for – to Muster Ameses to buy a shovel for alf a crown – that wus it now wusn't it? And doon't ee goo a worritting about ghosts at this time o day – twelve o'clock at night's their time for coming out.'

Joe began to rehearse his piece lest he should again forget, when just in the nick of time the little donkey and his driver reappeared on their homeward journey, and being acquainted with the story, Mrs Roberts said indignantly, 'Well I never! If that's your master's idea of a joke you can tell him from me that he'll never be likely to see a bigger idiot than himself.' She tore off a piece of the white paper in which her tea was wrapped, wrote down the message, and carefully wrapped the half crown, which Joe produced after much fumbling and several shocks from the fear that it too was lost. 'Now just give that to Mr Ames when you get to the shop,' she said, 'and he'll know just what you want, so don't worry if you do forget. That's what the dolt who sent you should have done if he'd had the sense of a snail.'

Joe set upon his way rejoicing, the half ounce of shag handed over to Sam, and the donkey trotted homewards in good style. Sam seeing the sun high in the heavens knew it was twelve o'clock and time for him to partake of his midday meal.

Just then a dogcart drove by, driven by a prosperous looking man who said in a flat voice to his companion, 'By jingo! What a monotonous life for a man, breaking stones by the roadside from year's end to year's end – on the same mile or two of road too. I've seen him breaking stones just here about ever since I was first breeched, and used to drive along with my old governor. Deadly monotony! What do you say, old boy?'

His companion agreed in a similarly lifeless voice. But Sam, now eating his dinner of cold suet pudding garnished by the bacon, which he had cut into neat dice with his pocket knife, was thinking how full and colourful the morning had been. When he had finished he would walk along the verge and pick some of that 'yarrer' – 'a drop of Polly's yarrer tea always went down good.' No sign yet of his friend-cum-enemy, the Surveyor.

One summer's day

The children scampered through the rain singing in their little tinkling voices which sounded for all the world like the music from an old fashioned musical box. 'Rain. Rain. Go to Spain,' and then, as the sun came out turning to silver the slanting streaks of rain, 'It's a sunshiny shower, won't last half an hour'. But look! A rainbow! They stopped to gaze in pleased surprise as they always did – and always would until they were little grey old women leaning their knobbly hands upon their sticks.

'That's God Himself,' said Eileen in an awestruck voice.

'What a lot of colours He is. I wish He'd give me a bit of that plum colour to make me a Sunday frock, that I do.'

'What do you think He's doing of up there, Eileen?' asked the youngest child.

Eileen who was the eldest and much the most sophisticated had usually an answer to give, and although she was a little nonplussed, answered solemnly 'He's charting in Heaven to be sure'.

'Teacher told us that the rainbow is God's promise. What did he promise us, Eileen?'

'I don't quite know,' confessed Eileen, who was after all only seven, and this was a question that many seventy-year-olds wouldn't be able to give a ready answer to – especially if they based it on results. 'But,' she added brightly, 'I'll ask our Linda when she comes home. She knows everything. I know what I want – a little white cat.'

'Well, you needn't bother God for that coz I'll give you one of our Tibbie's kittens when she has them. I know she'll have some before long because her belly's as round as a bumbarrel – and our mum says "Put her down" every time I pick her up.'

'It must be every bit white,' insisted Eileen. 'Because when I asked my mother if I can have a cat all to myself she says, "Only when you can find one without a single hair of any other colour on it".'

The children scattered to their several cottage homes and Eileen, who had the farthest to go, went on alone. How shiny the box hedges in the cottage gardens looked after the rain, and the bird cut out of a tree in old John Price's garden looked as if it had just risen from a brook. The child drew in a deep breath – the fragrance of the Earth seemed almost unbearably lovely; she remembered that moment all her life. When she got to her home her mother was rather cross for she was in the midst of a most critical operation. She was experimenting with one of those new-fashioned home dyes called 'maypole soap' that she had seen advertised and her hands had been itching to try it when funds allowed (always the deciding factor in their home). She had just ladled from the dye bath her three little girls' dresses which the directions on the packet had promised to turn, as if by magic, into a delightful red and unrecognisable from new... but alas promises, on dye packets as elsewhere, are rarely quite fulfilled. The dresses, which before their adventure had been a blue from which the blue had almost faded away, were now a queerish shade of pink and the mother was – not for the first time – deeply annoyed at the deception of the printed word. However, as she carried them dripping round the corner of the house to hang on the clothes line, she remarked hopefully that 'like the old woman's dishcloth they would probably look better when dry'.

'And what are you doing home from school at this time of day?' she asked bringing her attention to rest upon the child.

'We've got a holiday, Mamma, because it's Ascension Day and when we came back from church this morning governess told us we might go home. The others stayed behind because it was raining but Agnes, Gannie and I ran and ran, and now we are here first.'

'You didn't get your clothes wet coming through that shower, did you?'

'Oh no, I ran between the drops.' But if the child's clothes were dry enough her spirits were a little damped, for she felt her mother was anything but pleased at this unexpected holiday. And everything had been so lovely – the excitement of running through the rain, the rainbow, the unexpected sunshine, and the sweet perfume which had awakened such a beautiful feeling within her.

The mother was now busy making a cake for tea and Eileen crept upstairs where in the wide window seat behind the white curtains she kept her dolls. Now for a little while she sat down there and was deeply engrossed in making one of them an ultra fashionable hat like those worn by ladies in John Noble's catalogue. The catalogue came by post summer and winter giving untold pleasure to most of the family, for in the winter, after the evening meal was cleared away, they would sit round the table with pencils and paper copying anything they could get. The fine ladies and gentlemen were in great demand to colour, when they were fortunate enough to have a penny with which to buy a box of paints and as cut-outs for their scrap books. Then Mother got some good ideas from it too when she was making down some of the elders' clothes for the youngers, and Eileen for her dolls.

Tired of doing this, she began to read. There was a book of poems and French grammar left there by her sister Linda and she puzzled over them for a bit, wishing she could understand their meaning, then picked up her 'Ministering Children' which had been given her for her very own when one of the elders had outgrown its contents. Linda would be coming home tomorrow and when it was too wet for them to walk in the fields and wood, they would sit here in the window seat as quiet as mice, Linda reading and Eileen sewing or playing at being a nurse to her sick dolls. They were mostly maimed in one way or another, poor little waifs, some with their china heads tied on most precariously to their sawdust-stuffed bodies, or at least either arm or leg was missing; in their palmiest days they had not been very beautiful, having cost but a penny or twopence. The one with the wax face, that had been in her stocking at Christmas, was now slowly but surely melting away.

Then Linda and she would gaze wistfully out at the waving corn which grew right up to the iron fence that surrounded their house. Beyond the cornfields were woods, blue in the distance. A blue haze shimmered over the green or yellow fields and blue woods, turning the whole landscape into a lovely indescribable colour that made her think of the stones in Aunt Jane's ring, which she afterwards learnt were opals.

On very clear days they could see Brill Hill in the distance – very fascinating because her big brother Edward, who was nearly as old as Linda, used to tell the little ones that if they ran round the hill three times without stopping, they would be able to see the wind. Eileen was determined, and perhaps the others were too, to do this as soon as she was old enough to do everything she wished to – but alas! that time never has come, and her only memory of Brill is of seeing it from the little bedroom window. The distant hill that has never lost its greenness.

She could hear one of her sisters downstairs talking to her mother in a complaining voice about something or other that had happened at school. She crept downstairs softly and out of doors without being noticed. By a little summerhouse at the back of the house another small sister was playing happily by herself; a square of patchwork draped around her, she was addressing an imaginary person as Mrs Gotobed. The children rarely played together, for they were of entirely different temperaments and each had, even then, their own way of life. Eileen tiptoed past Queenie's cottage and on around the hamlet.

An oldish woman came out of one of the cottages, she was immensely large below the waist and had a cosy bust and short neck, over which hung a row of chins almost hiding the large silver Mizpah brooch that pinned her collar. Her dress of thick stuff of some nondescript colour was bunchy around the waist and over it she wore a large white apron. Her face was one of those ageless ones and it was plain to see that she hadn't a care in the world. Without a smile the fat woman and child curtsied deeply to each other, then solemnly shook hands. The woman backed a yard or two and, lifting her skirt daintily with both hands as if about to dance a minuet, she began to sing, a little quavery, the 'Keel Row'. They stepped towards each other, the woman as light as a cork on her feet, while the little girl had a somewhat elephantine tread, they met and whirled round on each other's arms, then parted without a word spoken but each laughing gaily. The fat lady began to sing cheerfully as she twirled her mop on the flagstones outside her cottage: 'When I was young and in my prime my work was done by dinner time, but now I'm old and quite forgot, I have to wear a billycock.'

The little girl sauntered along the gravel lane which led to the turn-pike picking a posy of wild flowers as she went and looking for larks' nests behind the gorse bushes; she found one with three eggs in it and her heart gave a little jump of joy, she looked at it tenderly for a minute or two without touching. She sniffed at the gorse blooms and picked them off the thorns carefully, then began to fill her pocket with them to make some perfume. She had an empty scent bottle and could get some water out of the rainwater butt. No other ingredients were necessary!

Doing this she suddenly became aware of someone watching her, and looking up saw a strange man sitting on the bank in an alcove of the hedge. Her first impulse was to run back to the village as fast as she could, but for the moment she was glued to the spot with surprise and in that moment she had found courage, for she had seen something very wonderful lying on the grass beside him, a bottle like those used for beer or vinegar, and afterwards utilised for home made wine – a beverage that was very popular around the neighbourhood – but this bottle contained something quite strange, a little white ship! How could it have got in there?

The man was busy making another ship, there was a smile on his broad red face as he said in a gruff voice, 'Don't e be afraid on me. Little gal, I beant a going to urt e. Just you come and look at what I be a doing of. There, that's the *Jane Malon* the prettiest barque that ever set sail, just like a bird ent she, my dear?'

'Yes,' murmured Eileen shyly as she gazed with longing upon the lovely little ship in full sail upon its miniature sea. 'How did you get it into the bottle?'

'Well, it's a funny thing now but most folks ask that self-same question,' laughed the jolly old man. 'Why, t'is as easy as pie, my dear, if only you knows how, but of course you haves to be a bit of a wizard – stands to reason, don't it now?'

'I wish I could make one' said the child wistfully, for she was more taken by the little ship than anything she had ever seen.

'Well, you just run and ask your mammy, my poppet, if she has got a empty bottle she can spare, and bring it to me full of water. Tell er a old sailor, me dear, is earning his bit o bread and baccy as he walks along to see his old mother.'

Eileen ran off full of hope that her mother would buy one of the ships from the old man, but no, she hadn't money to spare for such things; it was hard enough to raise the wind for necessaries, but he could have the bottle and welcome.

A little cast down but still hoping against hope that something incredible would happen to give the ship into her possession, the child went back more leisurely than she had come, swinging the bottle of water in her hand and thinking hard of ways and means. While her mother had rinsed and filled the bottle she had stolen upstairs and collected one or two treasures that belonged to her. A mother of pearl catshead brooch with green eyes which Aunt Jane had brought her on her last visit (it was now minus its pin), a tin pencil holder with a blue stone at the end – she had always nursed the exciting hope that one day this would turn out to be a precious stone of immense value and be the means of retrieving the family fortunes, and that she would eventually ride in her carriage and pair. People always said 'Riding in a carriage and pair' when ever they talked about being better off – not that she could see much fun in it, to run on her sturdy legs and jump over stiles and brooks was more to her taste. Well, she would barter away her chance of riches for the little ship she had fallen so in love with.

But – when she reached the spot where she had left them, both man and ship had disappeared. Gone like a pleasant dream on waking, and nothing remained to show that they had ever been, except the place on the bank where the grass was flattened and a few shavings of white wood. The child lay down on the grass and sobbed in her bitter disappointment.

But comfort came as it usually does in extremity. A ministering angel with long ringlets and a voice like silver bells bent over her and coaxed her to her feet. This was Gertrude, the twelve-year-old daughter of the innkeeper and Eileen's queen and heroine; she was taking her little brother for a walk and now took Eileen in the other hand. They walked and talked and the little girl soon forgot her trouble. Gertrude helped them to pick flowers and shewed them a bumbarrel's nest with lots and lots of tiny eggs in it. She picked an early wild rose from the hedge and pinned it to the child's frock. Each time her back was turned for a minute, Joseph, the little boy, gave Eileen a vindictive thump.

The village, or properly speaking hamlet for it had no church, was like a tiny island marooned in a sea of cornfields, the narrow gravelled road which went through it only led on to villages and hamlets as small and obscure as itself, and was rarely used except by the inhabitants of the district. Nevertheless from time to time strange people appeared, as if they had dropped from the clouds or clambered over the wall of the horizon. One day, looking out of the window at the snow which was driving across the fields and hiding the distant woods altogether, the children were delightfully excited at the large flakes, as they fluttered like birds and settled softly on the ground and window sills. They chanted together, 'Here comes the woman picking her geese – selling the feathers a penny a piece', when round the corner of the house came a tiny old lady with a scarlet shoulder shawl tied around her, and on her arm a basket of oranges.

The mother opened the door with difficulty, for the snow had drifted against it, and the children quickly clambered down from the window seat and gathered around her – oranges were a very special treat reserved for Christmas and other festive occasions, and then brought into the house secretly and hidden from view until the moment was come for their consumption, none had ever been brought to the door before – and here they were at a halfpenny each. Although quite tiny and hard looking, they were a lovely colour which delighted the children's eyes, as did the scarlet shawl with the snow flakes thick upon it.

The old woman's face and hands were brown and full of wrinkles, and her little slow black eyes darted hither and thither like those of the birds that sat on the iron railing waiting and watching for a crumb.

'Where ever have you come from on such a morning as this?' asked the mother. 'Why, you must be perished of cold.'

The old woman smiled but evaded the question. 'They be as sweet as honey, Maaam,' she said, bringing her basket arm forward. 'Buy one apiece for the chuldern, do now, only a apenny apiece.'

'I don't know that I've any halfpennies to spare,' was the usual formula but she longed to buy things to please her children. However money was so terribly short, there were four of them at the orange eating age, and she could spend twopence more profitably in many ways. In the end one of the children excitedly thrust forward a penny from her private exchequer and the mother then produced another from her much worn purse.

The children were happy and returned to their lookout by the window, but the mother was anxious about the old woman. 'Where are you going to now?' she asked. 'You will be buried in the snow, it's drifting everywhere. I'll make you a cup of hot cocoa to warm you up inside – the kettle is boiling on the hob so it won't take me a minute.'

But it was like trying to entice a robin within doors, the old woman wouldn't stop for the cocoa, or tell whence she came or whither she went, but smiling secretly she just melted away into the snow as she had come – never to be forgotten by at least one of the children.

All that winter it snowed and snowed until the drifts rose above the hedges, the hamlet was entirely cut off from the rest of the world, the children could not go to school, the father pushed his way through it as long as it was humanly possible, but in the end the road to the town was completely blocked and he had to stay away from his work. No horse and cart could penetrate the walls of snow so that the butcher, grocer, coalman, and most serious of all, the baker, could not reach them. The food situation was critical, famine almost at the door.

There was a consultation between the parents (not without some heat on either side). The father was for digging his way through the snow to the village where the baker lived, the mother thought it an impossibility and that he would be buried in it far away from help and freeze to death, then they'd have no more bread at all with no one to earn it. She could rub up a bit of something with the remaining flour and they still had a few potatoes. Tomorrow there might be a change.

However the father was adamant. He was really anxious to get food for his children. Besides, the adventure appealed to him: since he had begun to think about it, his mind had grown excited at the prospect, the forced inactivity of those last days had frayed his nerves and temper considerably, and here was an outlet.

The mother at last agreed on condition that some other man went with him, and while he, with birch broom and spade, made a path round to the cottage where Sam the roadman lived, she sat down with needle and thread and quickly made a bag from an old sheet with slings to put his arms through so that both hands might be free. Very soon he and Sam, both dressed up like snowmen and armed with spades, set out. They were many hours on their mission for they had to dig every step of the way, the mother's anxiety grew as dusk began to fall and even the children fell silent around the fire. Then big brother Edward came in from the farm where he helped Uncle John with the horses. He and the other men of the village who worked on the farms had concentrated on keeping a path clear for themselves to come and go, for it would never have done to leave the poor animals to their fate. When Edward had cast his snowy garments and was once more dressed in dry clothes, he sat down close to the blazing fire and brought out, to the children's delight, some sweet chestnuts, which they cooked on the trivet and were merry over it – almost forgetting father out in the snow.

All at once the door opened, and in came father, Sam and a young soldier, who was home on furlough and had gladly joined in the adventure. All were as merry as griggs and loaded with bread, enough for the whole hamlet.

'Come, bring out a bottle of that slan wine of yours, Em,' commanded the father with the air of a baron about to entertain his faithful retainers. 'Come on me boys, drink up, and warm the cockles of your hearts.'

But it was on a summer evening when another strange visitor descended upon the village. It was almost dusk and the children were going in one by one from their games of 'Drop handkerchief', 'Nuts in May', 'See what a Pretty Little Girl Have I', and many others in which they had all revelled all the evening, when an old gentleman in clerical garb appeared in the village street. He had a white beard and a far away look in his eyes. He tried to ask the children the way but didn't seem quite sure where he was bound for, and when they answered he could not hear. In desperation, feeling that here was something they could not understand, they ran to the door of a cottage where the woman was always kind and helpful. Mrs Godden and her family were at supper and she asked the old man in to a seat at her table that he might share their meal, but he would not eat nor speak (although it was remembered afterwards that he had tried to speak to the children), neither did he appear to understand when they questioned him. Mrs Godden called in Eileen, whom she considered the most likely of the children as a scribe, to write a series of little notes hoping he would be able to read them and write replies, but no advance was made. Eventually he was shown by signs and tokens that he might stay the night in the already overcrowded cottage, and Mrs Godden's son Joe gave up his sleeping place without a murmur so that this stranger could rest the night.

It was now quite dark and the children were shooed home to bed by parents who had come out to look for them, and had themselves joined in the little crowd around Mrs Godden's door. In the morning as soon as it was light the old man went off across the fields towards the woods in the opposite direction to that in which he had come. No hint of his identity did he give.

Years afterwards, Eileen pondered on this incident and wondered who it could have been – if the clergyman of some neighbouring parish, he would have been known to the people of the hamlet. If he had suffered a lapse in memory, which seemed the most reasonable supposition, and wandered from some more distant place, surely he would have been more travel stained. She could vividly remember that his clothes had been of the blackest black, his shoes polished, his hat very new looking and his short white beard well trimmed, in fact his general appearance immaculate. Her sharp little eyes had particularly noted all this because for a moment, in the fading light, she had thought him to be an old clergyman who had once lived amongst them; he was of the same height, rather tall, but his clothes were always threadbare and shabby, because he gave too much to others, and his cheeks were thin and hollow too. So this sleek well-dressed man couldn't be he. If the man had wandered from home and been missing for the night, surely some enquiries would have been made for him by friends and relatives, but no such enquiries were made. Was it a wolf in sheep's clothing, who had been in the midst of these unsuspecting villagers that night? Some criminal in disguise or the forlorn lost soul, or body rather, that he appeared to be? Surely those distant looking blue eyes couldn't have lied, yet the clerical garb was extremely new, and his behaviour was, to say the least of it, very strange indeed.

Sometimes on Sunday afternoons a little band of missionaries would come tramping down the gravelled road and form themselves into a ring by the well, and one of their number would blow a cornet, while the others sang some good rollicking hymns, much to the delight of the children. They usually were their only audience, and they were greatly intrigued when the insurance man, the sweep, or the grocer's journeyman, whom they knew in his everyday role, addressed God on behalf of the inhabitants of this hamlet, who were without a doubt dwelling in the darkest depths of wickedness. 'Though your sins be as scarlet,' they would cry passionately, and young Joe would begin to think of that marble he had cheated Harry Aires out of, and the little girls felt anxious about the fibs they had told their playfellows about the prowess of mother, or elder sister, or the halfpenny change from the milk they had surreptitiously spent on sweets at the feast.

Repentance was but brief, however, when the ardent little band closed their hymn books and shut up the 'musical' instrument in its black box. They then dropped to earth, or sought out the cottages of their earthly clientele, in good hopes of an invitation to a cup of tea and a good substantial wedge of dough cake – a delicacy that was always on the Sunday teatable. That would revive their strength for the long walk back to the town. The children soon forgot their role as sinners ripe for Hell fire, at least until they were in bed and walking into that dim corridor between waking and sleeping, where all sorts of difficult problems were apt to assail them.

Going to school

Although there were three ways, running almost parallel with each other, the children always went by the road way to school, it was unthinkable that they should go by either of the others although they often came home by them. The road consisted of three little hills in quick succession like a giant's stairway. They used sometimes to speculate as to whether the giants, who once lived in the neighbourhood (there was the tomb of one of them in the church a few miles away), walking that way had not accomplished the journey, which to the children seemed so interminable, in three rapid strides. It was common knowledge that in life the occupant of the tomb and his brother, who lived at another village two miles distant, used to sit on summer evenings each at his own cottage door and chat together.

A stranger traversing the road, or any grown person for that matter, would think it a particularly dull and uninteresting track, the hills scarcely hills at all and nothing worth notice in the landscape beyond the hedgerows. But the children found plenty of diversions. In later years few of them remembered anything they had learnt in school, but going to and coming from school they acquired a wealth of knowledge which never forsook them.

They started out in little family groups at least an hour before school opened and one or two mothers, who were anxious that their children should not learn any rude words, sent them off well in advance, so that they were usually to be seen on the distant third hill while the others were descending the slight incline of the first; thus were they more or less segregated from the naughty ones. The eldest one of each family carried a brown canvas school satchel which contained the family lunch, to be eaten at midday – *al fresco* unless it rained or snowed relentlessly, when they were allowed to sit at their desks, but they had to be quiet as mice.

At the bottom of the first incline there was the shepherd's cottage in the midst of the rickyard, and there was always something going on to attract them. Sometimes ricks were being built and the children stopped to watch the elevator carrying up the hay or straw and placing it on the pile in a way which seemed almost miraculous. In the autumn the thrashing engine with its accompanying box would be there and they would watch fascinated by its almost human activity as it delivered the grain into open-necked sacks hanging in a row at the back of the box and sent the straw and chaff each to their own places. It was a miniature inferno, the men shouting at each other to make themselves heard above the puffing and shunting of the engine and the perpetual buzzing of the box, the engine driver with face and hands as black as soot, and the other men covered with sweat and chaff. Mice flashed from the rick which was rapidly being demolished, for the temporary sanctuary of another which was as yet intact, followed by boys brandishing sticks and whooping like wild Indians. The mice usually got away unless they had the misfortune to run into the very jaws of one of the farmyard cats who sat decorously around corners, having more subtle methods of game hunting than the boys.

It was wildly exhilarating to the boys and the bolder girls, but the shy little girls shrank back as from a bad dream. Maybe they had here a foresight of the state of discord and confusion into which their world was to be plunged in years to come.

Sometimes the engine driver would let one or two of the boys stand on the engine beside him where they felt like Kings of Creation, for that was in the days when to be an engine driver was every boy's first ambition.

But the thrashing was not often in progress and on most mornings of the year the children took their delights in smaller doses, the chasing and being chased by the turkey cock who walked on occasions with his lady and growing family on the grass verge outside the gate, or the teasing of the black and white sheep dog when nothing else offered. Once or twice the shepherd's wife had waited at the gate with a handful of cherries and, not so rarely, with a few apples in her apron to give them. In lambing season the shepherd himself would sometimes be there with a bunch of lamb's tails for one or another to take home to mother to make a pie of – but of course that was on their return journey.

Now to make up the time already squandered, the children scampered over the next hill as fast as their sturdy little legs would take them, but when they came to the hollow, they could not resist lingering a little to look over the gate that opened into a stone pit. In one corner of the pit stood the lime kiln: it had not been worked during their memory, and was derelict. It now had wild flowers growing over it, but they had heard grown people talk of the men who had once come from the wilderness of the outside world and burnt lime in it – men with queer names like Spider and Crook, legendary men, seeming as remote as the ancient Britons to the children's minds. Although it was but a very few years since their departure.

On the return journey they sometimes went into the stone pit and played running to the top of the kiln and jumping down, see-sawing on a plank that had been lying there for years, or picking bunches of wild flowers – they all loved flowers, and were delighted to find the first of the season of any species. The flowery patch of the lime kiln was always in their minds when they played 'Up a top o Robin's Hill, picking Robin's flowers. Robin's gone to light his pipe and won't be back for hours.' And Robin, who always came back suddenly and caught them trespassing if they were not quick, was one of the prehistoric men who had worked there.

But they must not dally too long on the way to school so they again took to their heels and galloped over the last hill for all the world like a pack of Dartmoor ponies loose on the moor, the steel tips of their strong little boots clanking merrily on the hard stones of the road. Unless they had time well by the forelock, they resisted the temptation to peer under the hedges for violets, when in season, or to look for billybuttons or anything else they considered edible. Although they rarely passed one particular object without pausing a moment to look, and strange thoughts passed through their young minds, for this was a ploughshare set up under the hedge to mark the exact spot where a young boy was killed. Tommy Cowley had not long left school when one afternoon while in charge of a farm cart he met some of his erstwhile fellow scholars on their way home and, wishing to show off to them his prowess, he stood up boldly on the shafts of the farm cart balancing himself like a circus rider. The old horse not being used to such dare-devilment quickened his pace abruptly and the poor boy fell on his head on the road. He died instantly. He looked so strange lying there, the frightened children ran away crying, for like Wordsworth's little maid so full of life, 'What should they know of death?' except that there was a place called the 'Pity-hole' into which Grannies and Grampies, and infants who had scarcely lived at all, were put – and yet were said to be singing and playing golden harps in Heaven. But to see a boy who had run and shouted, thrown stones and robbed birds' nests with them, who was healthily naughty and good by turns, snatched away by death before their very eyes – to be in the presence of the grim snatcher was an awesome experience which made a deep and lifelong impression on them, particularly on the imaginative ones. The men who had been following in the cart at a short distance with other horses were soon upon the spot and, before they carried away the empty shell that so short a time ago had held the blythe spirit of a young and happy boy, one had placed the ploughshare in the hedge. There it remained for many a long year – it may still be there, its purpose long forgotten.

Now the children had reached the end of the long road and at this point another crossed it like the top of a letter T. The right hand branched towards the schoolhouse, and was more pleasing, to a mature person that is to say, than the long barren road they had just traversed, part of it was overhung by trees and there was a distant view of shady woodland on either hand, but the children liked it less perhaps because it brought them, in a few minutes, to the prison most of them so much detested. It was under the thrall of grown ups and it brought an end to their hour of perfect freedom, for going to and from school they lived a life all their own, putting on personalities which at home or at school would scarcely have been recognisable. Some of them, who were subdued enough at home, now became regular little martinets, truculent and aggressive, while those who were seemingly bold enough when bolstered up by the presence of parents or other more influential

Cottisford School. Betty and Flora attended this school.

members of their families, now crept into their shells, and those who were too shy to speak in the presence of grown-ups were now full of chatter. The imaginative ones romanced to their hearts' content without fear of being punished for lying and the inveterate fibbers had a free rein. Many of the girls became exact replicas of their mothers – using the same words, voice and mannerisms. Altogether it was a fair preview of the adults that the children would become in after years.

If anyone had asked them to take the left hand turning at the top of the long road, they would have steadfastly refused – nobody went that way, why nobody quite knew. All the years of their school life the children passed it night and morning, but all through that time they never went down it; very rarely one or two of them, out of bravado, would dare the others to go down 'Dickie Brackels' with them and they would bravely run a few yards to where the road curved, but nothing would induce them to go further – beyond that curve something terrible was lurking. What could it have been?

Few grown-ups went that way either. There was certainly something sinister about it – it may only have been caused by the tall dark hedges that hung over either side of the narrow road making it dark and airless. There was a whisper of a hanging, but nothing more was known by the children or their parents who had heard the same whisper in their childhood. It may have been some poor distressed soul had taken his own life and his tormented spirit lingered here. Or had it once been the road trodden by men, women and even little children, condemned to death for such small and human offences as stealing food from the rich man who had abundance while they were driven to desperation by hunger, on their anguished journey to the gibbet? Nobody knew nor did they speak of it, but all felt that strange sadness and depression in the air which frightened the children so.

When they reached the schoolhouse, breathless through running the last hundred yards of the way, a monitress would be standing at the white wicket gate ringing the hand bell. She would give them just time to snatch off their hats and coats, hang them on their individual pegs in the lobby and dart into the school where those who had been in the advance party were already sitting at their desks looking cool, calm and dapper, waiting for Governess, who stood with visible patience in the foreground, to begin prayers. After a children's hymn had been sung and the Lord's Prayer said in unison, there would be part of the Church Catechism gone through and the scripture lesson proper would begin – more time and thought was given to this lesson than to any other taught in the school, so much so that at the end of their school days all but the least intelligent must have known the Bible by heart from cover to cover. Twice a week the Rector would be there to take a class of the elder scholars for scripture while Governess would cope with the rest in a communal lesson.

The Rector then stayed to give these elders their English lesson, and very fortunate were the intelligently minded in having such a tutor – especially at that particular period, for here was a man of exceptional scholarship with a vivid sense of humour and a charming personality. Many of the Young Ladies' Seminaries in the county could not have given better tuition at a far greater cost. But alas! not many of these children had eyes that saw or ears that heard and their chief object seemed to be to learn as little as they possibly could.

In the classroom, in a corner of their own shut off by a green baize curtain, the 'Infants' were learning the alphabet or to read such little

words as cat, dog, pig, tub and fly under the guidance of the monitress. When this really serious part of the lessons was over, they would
be able to relax with a Japanese saucer of beads of all colours to
thread, or bright shiny mats to weave of red, blue, yellow and green
paper, or sew with gaily coloured wools the parrots' heads, cups and
saucers, kettles, etc. outlined on cards. They could build houses and
bridges with stone-coloured and terracotta bricks, or outline all sorts
of weird and wonderful designs of their own with the bundles of
matchlike sticks. Seemingly futile occupations but they had their own
worth in teaching dexterity of hand – and it was with their hands that
most of these tiny mites were to earn their bread. During such lessons
as scripture, singing and musical drill the green baize curtain was
drawn aside on its brass rod and the little ones thus revealed to
Governess's critical eye.

It was a pleasant room with light-coloured painted walls on
which, between the maps of all countries, whose blue seas and red
markings gave a pleasant splash of colour, were several black and
white drawings in appropriate frames drawn by an old pupil at the
school. One end of the room was entirely taken up by a large window
– just too high for the children to see out of, it had a wide sill which
was usually adorned with a variety of objects which had been confiscated from the little scholars who had brought them to help while the
tedium of their durance, but had not the diplomacy to conceal them
until the moment when Governess's back was wholly turned.

On the opposite side of the door were three smaller windows, and
through them in the garden without, one could always see the
branches of the apple trees bobbing and dancing in every breeze.
Sometimes they tapped the windows as if they were in league with the
children and were calling them out to play. On a memorable day – it
must have been very late in the spring, for the apple blossom was
already in bud and none of the adults could remember snow falling
so late in the year – the children were amazed and delighted to wake
up to a white world. Anything out of the common in their placid little
lives was to them a miracle. During the morning fresh showers fell
and Eileen looking up at one of the windows saw, all to herself, the
loveliest picture there, big white flakes were whirling, dancing and

tumbling over each other in the air, then settling lightly on the branches and leaves of the apple tree until it was all outlined with white, except where the soft pink knot of buds peeped through. Then, as if the tree of itself were not altogether beautiful, a red squirrel suddenly appeared on a low branch close to the window washing the snow from his nose with his tiny paws, his bright eyes glistening as he peered for a few seconds at the children bent over their lessons, when seeming to catch the eye of the little girl watching he darted a little further up the tree and peeped again. Then, as if for her special benefit, he leapt from bough to bough of the snow-clad tree as lightly as the snow flakes that danced around him, and in another moment he was gone. The suddenness and intense beauty of the scene remained, like a picture painted on glass, on the child's mind for ever.

The room was never bare of flowers, there were nosegays in every window and on Governess's table; even in the dead of winter there was a flower or two to brighten up the gally pots of evergreen. Governess herself rarely came into school without a flower in her wide petersham belt, and the monitresses who were modelling themselves on her pattern, and one or two of the elder girls who were beginning to feel the importance of dress, wore theirs in the same fashion. Most of the smaller girls also began school in the morning with a posy pinned to the shoulder of their overalls.

At eleven o'clock there was a fifteen minute recess and a raid was made on dinner satchels to see if mother had put in a little surprise packet containing a few sweets, or sugared biscuits, or at least a finger of cake to beguile the time. They munched this under the silver birches in the playground, a little group of the toughest among them took possession of the swing in the centre while the others played 'tig' and such like games using the trunks of the trees for touch posts, but all too soon a curt ting-a-ling from the bell brought them into line again.

If the playtime had gone in a flash the next forty-five minutes hung heavily enough; if there was one lesson they abhorred above all others it was history. What did old dead kings and queens matter to them? Nasty quarrelsome lot always having somebody's head cut off even when they weren't having a real war, and killing men wholesale. They were told wars were out of date now, and there would never be another, and also how lucky they were to live in such peaceable times; never would their lives be disturbed by war. Alas! most of them were destined to see at least three, each one more terrible than the last.

But twelve o'clock came at long last and they sang 'Grace' with gusto: 'Be present at our table, Lord'. Although the table was but metaphorical no doubt the Lord was even more present with them as they sat under trees, or on sunny banks, or ran to and fro while they ate their frugal meal. A few of the children lived quite near to the school and two or three others had relatives nearby. These went home for their meal, but were gone and back again like bandersnatchers so as not to be left out of the play.

There were no communal games, such as 'Drop Handkerchief', 'Green Gravel', 'Sally Sally Waters' or any of the others they played in the evenings. During the dinner hour they split up into little groups and played 'House' in a long tunnel of bushes nearby, or sat on banks playing 'Dabs' with five flat stones, or wandered off to the brook and floated sticks and looked for minnows. An old clergyman who once had charge of the Parish during the illness of the late Rector, pitying the children at their desultory games, had presented the school with a whole cupboard full of bats and balls, shuttlecocks, skipping ropes with bells, and all sort of equally beguiling toys. There were, however, hampering rules attached to the giving out and replacing of these and soon, the novelty having worn off, the children went back to their own unordered games. Once in a while a spirit of adventure would ensnare them, and they would run off to a distant wood where wild cherries grew, although they knew that no matter how fast they ran they would never get back in time for the warning bell, which told them to go in and wash their hands ready for afternoon school. However, Governess, being kind beneath her outward veneer of severity, would delay a little the ringing of the bell until the children came running pell-mell, rosy cheeked and breathless, into view. But when, taking advantage of this leniency, they once ventured much further afield in search of wild strawberries, and were long overdue for school opening, they were greeted with frost like severity and made to feel like criminals on trial for the rest of the day.

The afternoon lessons were not so irksome as those of the morning. A very elementary lesson in drawing for the boys while the girls did needlework which they all rather liked, for authority was slackened during this hour. Although the fine needlework which had been the pride and joy of the school in past decades was now a thing of the past, the girls were interested in their task, for the garments which were taking so many months to make were for themselves to wear eventually – and what woman, however young, is not interested in her own apparel?

On certain days this hour was taken up by geography and map drawing – the latter had but lately been added to the curriculum, and was heavy going for the little scholars who were by no means born draughtsmen. With geography they were at their best. At three o'clock came another ten minutes' scamper round the silver birches while they filled their little lungs with fresh air to buoy them up through the last half hour's lesson – this was usually something airy and bright and much more to their liking such as singing or musical drill and was just a prelude to freedom.

And never was freedom more sweet when at long last it came. Sedately they answered Governess's 'Good afternoon' as they passed before her on their way out, but as the threshold was crossed, life bubbled up inside them anew and they ran and jumped and laughed for very joy.

Along the wide window sill, as well as personal treasures which had been confiscated earlier in the day and now returned to their owners, were a row of tin milk cans brought by some of the girls in the morning in readiness to fetch milk on their way home. There was something very special about 'fetching milk'; it was not at all the simple errand it sounds. To begin with they must go home by the field way, which was taboo in the morning, and there lay a set of delights quite distinct to those of the road.

So the little women set out with their cans jangling, for they often carried two in each hand – they were always ready to bring milk for anyone in the hamlet who hadn't a responsible ambassador of their own to send for it, for the halfpenny with which they were often rewarded was a welcome source of revenue.

The village, although its inhabitants claimed some sort of superiority over the hamleteers, was scarcely noticeable at all for it consisted of but the church and school, the Rectory, Squire's house, and less than a dozen cottages – these all widely scattered along a stretch of roadway that led even deeper into the back of beyond. Next to the school came a cottage which belonged to Tom, the parish clerk, and had the distinction of having the red post box in its side wall and Mr Plum, the postman, was usually clearing this of its half dozen letters as the little girls passed. They would circle round him to watch this unique operation and to peep to see if that letter Mother had given one of them to post to Aunt Kizzie in London was really taken from the depths of the box. Mr Plum juggled with the tablets foretelling the next day changing Monday to Tuesday, Wednesday to Thursday and so on, then shut the door with such a determined air and loud snap that it almost seemed in so doing he had actually changed that day into the next.

Next came a house of very superior character with sash windows on either side of the door which had a little porch over it. The walls were clad in ivy and clematis so neatly cut that not one single leaf was overgrown, and even the grass verge between the front gate and the road was always mown to a nicety. As long as Eileen could remember, when she and her sisters were pretending that one day a fairy would come down the chimney and give them each a wish, and they had asked their mother what hers would be, she had always said without a moment's hesitation, 'I should wish for Henry Tovey's house and a pound a week for life.'

Mrs Tovey held her head high. She had once been the village school Governess and had married, some thought beneath her, the Squire's general factotum, but this had not impaired her superiority in the least, for hadn't she taken Henry up to her own plane, making a clean cut between his work and their private life, training him in manners, and dress when off duty, to outsquire the Squire himself? And although folks sometimes sniggered at his church-going silk hat and lavender kid gloves, they couldn't help admiring the independence of the pair, and they were much esteemed. Mrs Tovey rarely went out except to church on Sunday mornings – in the mornings only was the cream of this small community there. She could often be seen amongst the flowers and beehives in her garden, and she would knock on the window at the children if they played noisily near her gate or trod on her private grass verge. She would also rebuke them sternly if she heard any rudeness or otherwise naughty goings on. She looked critically upon the behaviour of the older girls, seeming to regret her loss of power to make them somehow different to what they were, and they all were rather in awe of her. The little girls walked very decorously past her domain – soon they were to find to their great surprise that here was no ogre but a most delightful friend and companion, for she unexpectedly came back to school to fill a vacancy for a few months making the harvest to Christmas term the pleasantest of all their school days.

The milk maids went by the saw pit without stopping, for although it was sometimes a favourite place for play, it was out of fashion just then apparently. They came to the first farm where displayed upon a barn door were all sorts of printed notices, some of them must have been police notices for amongst them was one about the protection of wild birds – the law must only just then have been made. There were also notices about a general election, a cattle show, and several drapers' sales in which cotton prints were offered at one penny a yard, calicos at twopence halfpenny and threepence, gloves at threepence, shoes one and elevenpence, boys' trousers sixpence, ladies' hats from one penny upwards – it seems like a chapter from *Alice in Wonderland*. Just as the little girls were reading aloud the election poster, the late Rector's daughter, a sweet gentle woman of middle age, came along and paused beside them.

'Those dreadful Radicals, my dears,' she said, 'are simply ruining our country, I don't know where it will all end! I hope you will never believe anything they say. But there! It is a great blessing that women and girls know nothing about politics – and never will, I hope and pray. Although the world is in such a state of change of late years, one scarcely knows master from man now, and I'm sure that is not what God meant for us.'

'Eileen's dad's a radical, ent he, Eileen?' said one of the other girls mischievously. 'I heard him preaching about it tother night. My dad says he'd be on um too if he'd a dare – but it udn't do to offend them rank old toories, that it udn't, or us shouldn't get no butter on our bread.'

Poor Miss Grace looked sad and sighed, and then made a chiding little noise with her tongue. Eileen, feeling that the subject must be changed, said brightly, 'Our Linda is going to have a bicycle.'

But far from relieving the situation this remark further congested it, Miss Grace looked horrified, and even angry – as far as her gentle disposition would allow. 'You must be mistaken, child, surely your mother would never allow Linda to make such a disgraceful exhibition of herself!' she gasped.

'Oh it's not going to be one of those high ones that you have to climb a wall to get onto – it's going to be a ladies' safety bicycle,' Eileen placated.

'*Ladies*, my dear Eileen, do not ride bicycles. Never, never will you see a *Lady* so disgrace herself.'

'But a lot o women do,' put in the saucy one. 'I've seen um gooin along the turnpike and at Brierly, when I goo shoppin we our Mum, they look just like ladies that um do.'

'When you are a little older, Amy, you will learn right from wrong – and nothing will ever make this undignified pastime right.' Miss Grace went on her way sorrowfully, it had made her sad to see, during this brief visit to her old home, how even in this secluded parish standards had dropped and change and decay were rife – decay of all the old customs and beliefs which she had been born to and believed in with all her heart. Oxford, where she now lived, was full of sin, but she had hoped to find everything unaltered here – as it had been hitherto from the day of her birth. Girls she had helped to train so carefully, for whom she had striven to make her own life one long example, to think of them sitting astride bicycles with skirts blown aside displaying their white embroidered petticoats for all the world, as brazen as the fast women who lived in the towns! Moreover, it was not only their modesty they were losing rapidly, but humility, that equally precious gem for the adornment of the girl of lowly birth, had almost vanished.

As she crossed the field on her way to visit one of her sick poor at a lonely farm cottage, she thought with sudden longing of the days of her own girlhood. Visiting one day a neighbouring Rectory, where she had always been a most welcome guest, she had found the daughters of the house and Eileen's mother, Emma, who acted as nurse to the youngers and companion to the elders of the large family, grouped round the harmonium in the schoolroom singing, and she had joined in. Such pretty songs which are never heard nowadays, of course. Emma had such a sweet voice – what a pity that all her children were so unmusical. She had been one of the singers in the music festival that year and received much praise to which she always protested that 'she really couldn't sing a bit,' but that was only girlish modesty – she loved being thought much of. She as well as Miss Grace and her friend Edith Loveday were in their seventeenth year, the other three Loveday girls were in their still earlier teens. What a happy day that had been. When they tired of singing they had talked themselves hoarse, and in everything there had been a source of merriment. There was the girls' needlework to be brought out and admired, including the elaborate piano runner which the two elder girls were working in secret for Mama's birthday. The most recently read books were talked about, and a favourite one lent to the visitor in return for one she had brought for them to read. Edith drew Grace to a quiet corner where they talked secrets in a low voice under cover of the general chatter and laughter. Emma hearing the baby awake from his afternoon sleep ran to fetch him and all his sisters vied for the honour of holding him while she went down to hasten tea.

'But these are yesterday's cakes, surely,' said Lilly. 'And I'm sure I smelt cakes baking this afternoon. Why can't cook let us have some of those? I wonder if I went down and coaxed her a little – '

'No,' said Edith decidedly, 'she certainly would not. Cook would only say, "Away with your cajolery, Miss Lilly – ne'er shall one o my cakes be cut hot, not if the Queen herself requested it."',

'When I'm married,' said Emma, 'I shall always have hot cake for tea.'

'And I too,' declared Lilly, Edith, and Grace.

'Now that is a vow between us,' said Edith gravely, 'That we will all beguile our husbands with deliciously smelling cakes straight from the oven.' They all agreed – such recklessness would be delightful.

Only a few days ago Miss Grace had thought of it when she was visiting Emma, and asked her if she remembered too. 'Yes' replied Emma with a smile, 'I often have hot seed cake on the table for Sunday tea, and never do I cut it without thinking of that day.'

Some of the Loveday girls had married and some were still spinsters like herself. Emma, whom they were all so fond of, had made a queer marriage – most disappointing. Life had been very pleasant in those days, not excitingly so, but in a quiet gentle way they had been so very happy. Mr Loveday had later been given a much better living in another county, and so their paths had divided until now-a-days it was once in years that she saw any of the girls. They might have kept more in touch if her manifold duties, in her father's parish and to her family, had not entirely submerged her. Now here she was, a rapidly ageing woman with all her duties gone – melted away all at once like last year's snows. She still 'went about doing good' amongst the poor in Oxford, where she lived in rooms on her very slender income, but it was different, altogether different.

Yes, that had been a particularly happy day – seeing and hearing of Emma's daughters had brought it back so vividly to her mind – she wished those children were more like Emma, especially Linda who was altogether her father's child. The tune of one of the songs they had sung that day would keep running through her head and she found herself humming the refrain as she crossed the field.

Wave willows. Murmur waters. Loving sunbeam smile.
Earthly music ne'er can waken lovely Annie Lyle.

Most of their songs had a little sadness in them which they rather enjoyed – as a contrast to their lives of gentle happiness, perhaps.

And coming home

The little girls had no past to sadden them and they were not yet of an age to be much engrossed with their future, but the golden hours of the present were entirely theirs. After they had run several times up and down the steep bank until they were out of breath, they sat on a low wall facing the weir listening to the hissing and thumping of water as it fell into the pond, beyond where, beneath dark overhanging trees, it flowed on they knew not where, for that was Squire's land and they never dared to set foot upon it. There was a round shallow pond outside the grating which sometimes, to their joy, overflowed the road and they walked recklessly through it instead of keeping to the footway under the high wall of the Tudor farmhouse. This was a path on which they would not have walked by themselves after twilight for all the sweets contained in all the sugar cane in the wide world. Even on moonlight nights, when some of them passed on their way to church, the square tower looming above the high surrounding wall would look gloomy and mysterious, and they would hold tightly to Mother's arm or snuggle up to Father. They would think of stories they had heard of the grim little prison room it contained and the yawning opening which led beneath – some said to a dungeon where the poor prisoners had been thrown, others to an underground passage to the church. However it might be, the house looked innocent enough in the sunlight with tufts of grass and an occasional self-sown flower growing on its wall – rather like something from Grimms' fairy tales.

After the Tudor farmhouse and the weir came the Rectory Meadow, sunny and friendly, although the old horse who had always been there as long as they could remember, his legs hobbled and his jumping days long since past, had gone together with all the other familiar possessions of the old Rector. The Rectory too had lost its old quiet – but still the ancient quince tree, which grew by the side gate, shed its fruit unheeded onto the pathway without, to be snatched up quickly by each generation of children as they passed – and to be hastily thrown away with the same wry face and disappointment.

The Rectory was now full of life and activity for the Rector had half a dozen young male pupils, and a tennis lawn had been laid out for them and the old barn had been turned into a badminton court. At this time in the afternoon there was sure to be a gay clatter of voices and bumping of balls from one or other of these, unless they happened to be setting out to some other sport in the neighbourhood; then they would come careering down the drive on their bicycles bearing racquets or some other gear in one hand, the other one resting with studied nonchalance on handle bars. Their clothes immaculate and the last word for whatever sport they were bent upon, never had such outfits been seen in the village before and the little girls were apt to gaze upon them with visible astonishment. It must be said that the young men were equally amazed at the appearance of the little girls, in fact each regarded each as some strange visitant from another world. But the little girls were intensely interested in them and by careful watching and listening had found out a great deal of their life stories. This little knowledge mixed with a good pinch of imagination made absorbing entertainment. As they grew towards the age for falling in love one or two of the girls were secretly enthralled with one or other of the young men who hadn't the slightest knowledge of the delicate attention they were receiving – taking no more notice of their admirers than they did of the Persian cat who sat sunning herself on the Rectory wall.

The bombardment of cycles had driven the milk carriers into a huddle on the grass verge but soon they regained their equilibrium and gazed with eager curiosity after them while they regaled each other with their latest findings. The precocious Amy had some weird and wonderful revelation to make which, young as they were, others queried for already she had the reputation of being an inveterate liar.

'That one stutters something awful,' said Agnes, proud of her knowledge. 'He can scarcely speak weout spluttering – Parson's trying to cure him on it.'

'That Mr Weaver belongs to folks as are as rich as rich can be, but he's a terrible dunce – Parson don't half give him gip,' said quiet little Emmie.

'Mother says they are all backward in some way,' put in Eileen. 'That's why they come to Mr Beckleston. He's that clever he can make them learn even if they couldn't at college where they'll go when he's finished with them.'

Opposite the Rectory was a little wicket gate by which the children entered the overgrown pathway between the churchyard and the shrubbery, which led to the back premise of the Manor House. At the junction where the grass grown drive which led to the front of the house crossed the path, they came face to face with a little girl who was exercising a fat white dog. She stared at the children with haughty disdain as she had seen her grandmother, the old Squiress do, and they stared back at her, but also at her clothes in candid admiration. Eileen decided forthwith to, after all, wear the old brown skirt which she had hidden under all her other clothes on a peg in her bedroom. She had pretended that she couldn't find it because she had thought it looked so odd with her knees showing while all the other children wore theirs almost covering the calves of their legs, more or less according to the age of the garment and the growth of its wearer. Now here was a glimpse into the mirror of fashion. In actual fact the little girl was dressed in a rather shabby tweed coat and skirt with her long thin legs and feet encased in well-worn shoes and brown stockings, which had been well darned at the knees. The only touch of flamboyance about her was a broad quill which was stuck through a knot of ribbon on her hat.

They passed the stables where a black retriever dog poked his nose through a hole, cut for that purpose, at the bottom of one of the doors. He barked at them and made them fly to the other side of the pathway, for although they had never seen more of him than his nose, they had a dreadful fear that one day he would be loose and tear them to shreds. He seemed so angry at their passing.

They stood and knocked at the back door but no one came although they could see, at the bottom of the rickety stairs in the basement kitchen, the housemaid in her black dress and stiffly starched regalia including a cap with streamers at least a yard of length which gave her a very fly away air. She was partly kneeling on a chair and leaning across the long deal table in earnest conversation with the kitchenmaid in a similar attitude on the other side. They took not the slightest notice of the children who, although they continued to knock at discreet intervals to proclaim their presence, were intensely interested in the conversation below. The children gathered a good many details of the strange way of life of the old squiress and her son as well as some mysterious details of the courtships of the two conversationalists. Insight was also given them into the nature of the cook-housekeeper, who was evidently a dyed-in-the-wool terrorist, and there were also veiled allusions to queer goings on of people in their own and other villages.

Presently there was the sound of the quick opening and shutting of a door at the other end of the kitchen, which was invisible to the children, and the two girls instantly began to work feverishly at the tasks which had been suspended while cook was changing her dress.

'Haven't the children been for milk yet, Sarah?' Sarah's name at home and to all her familiars was Ivy, but that was not considered seemly in her profession in which such names as Sarah, Emma, Jane etc., names long gone out of fashion and not likely to be borne by their betters, were considered more appropriate. Cook's voice sounded very cross as if she knew full well what the girls had been up to during her absence.

Sarah glanced upwards towards the waiting children and, as if she had that minute only become aware of their presence, she answered cheerfully, 'Well! Here they be a comin now, I do declare,' and she ran lightly up the stairs and collected the cans with a smile. Cook always filled them herself and sometimes brought them back – they couldn't trust that flipperty gibbet of a Sarah to give bare measure for the half-pennies and pennies proffered – although she herself put a little extra in each can for she knew that children drank some of it going home, and she didn't want their mothers to go short of a drop in their tea on that account – but then she knew what was what and who deserved extra and who didn't, while Sarah would just have baled it out without rhyme or reason. Yes, Mrs Hall's bark was far worse than her bite. She always wore what was a very old fashioned lilac print dress without apron, and was the thinnest woman imaginable with a face like a withered apple, or rather crab apple, for it had a permanently sour expression, and her hands were very wrinkled. She spoke crossly to the children as she handed them their cans, and then rather disdainfully held out a second one to Amy saying, 'Here's your Grannie's tea leaves, and don't go emptying them in the brook either.' By ancient custom the mistress of the house insisted that all spent tea leaves must be saved and given weekly to this old woman that she might draw a second brew out of them, but this beneficence which had pleased old Nancy down to the ground forty years earlier was now, when good tea cost but threepence a quarter, an unwanted gift to be treated with derision by her grandchildren who never carried it a step nearer than needs be. But old Nancy never failed to pour effusive thanks upon the Squiress whenever she descended upon her, although she had not seen the tea leaves this many a year.

Amy had large wide innocent grey eyes and a mouth which wouldn't have melted butter. She assured the cook that nothing – *nothing* was farther from her thoughts than to throw away this gift so coveted by her Grannie.

The children rarely passed the little iron gate, which groaned dismally whenever it was opened or shut and led into the churchyard from the overgrown pathway, but they must go through it. Just within was the old Rector's grave; only a short time since he had gone to lie beside the wife who had died tragically many years before. Regularly the children read the inscription which always puzzled them somewhat – 'Here we see as through a glass darkly, but then face to face'. What could it mean? Across the pathway underneath the east window lay their young son and daughter who had died long ago in the flower of their youth. These children had never seen them and yet they knew them well – as they did most of the people buried here who had died long, long before they were born, the living had such tales to tell of them – old Grampie Cross had been bold as a lion, afraid of nobody nor nought, old Grannie Braby had been the kindest human that ever was, this one had gone through fire and water to help someone in dire distress while another had a tongue that would

have got the better of the devil himself. Then there was the grave of
the woman who had been almost buried alive but fortunately she had
wakened from her trance just before the funeral began – she had,
however really died very soon afterwards so that the coffin came in
handy after all, it would have been a pity if the money spent on it
should have been wasted; even at their tender age they had the begin-
nings of frugal minds. Here was the young girl whose blood had
turned to water and there the boy who had swallowed a brass button
from his soldier uncle's greatcoat. This grave held a woman whose
name was not remembered and who had once lived in a cottage
which was now in ruins. She had been able to foretell the future.
Under the hedge was a row of tombstones, a whole family, but no one
living seemed to know who they were or where they lived.

The children would wander round the corner of the chancel to
where babies lay in rows of little green mounds and, if they had gathered a few wild flowers beforehand, they would lay them lovingly on
the grave of a tiny brother or sister whom they perhaps had not
known in life, but who was still 'Our Nellie' or 'Our Rose' or
'Charlie' to be owned and loved with the rest of the family. Sometime
the little graves were covered with forget-me-nots for all the world as
if the Divine Mother in tenderness for these babes, who had been so
early deprived of life, had covered them with her blue cloak.

Death was no stranger in the homes of the children and they were
not too saddened when 'Our Baby' who had been theirs but a few
days, weeks or months, died. They themselves enjoyed a little limelight amongst their playmates for a few days, gladly they went into
the fields to pick wild pansies and stars of Bethlehem to make wreaths
and crosses for the funeral, or they were the recipients of posies of
moss rose buds and periwinkles from their friends' gardens to carry
in their hands as they walked behind the tiny coffin. There was a
touch of pageantry for them too in the funeral. Four maidens
dressed in white carried the tiny white coffin, with its silvered fittings,
in a white tablecloth of which they each held a corner in their white
gloved hands. Thus they walked to the church no matter how far,
followed by parents and little brothers and sisters all dressed in the
deepest of black. If they had no money to buy this mourning attire it

did not matter as everybody in the village and hamlet was willing and eager to lend any black garment they had, so that most times nothing had to be spent in fitting the whole family up except perhaps a few pence on a black bordered handkerchief each, for them to cry into. Only the mother's sadness and tears saddened the children.

There were few gravestones in the churchyard because most of the inhabitants had been poor in life and only the rich hitherto had been able to afford such grandeur, but now that the thrifty ones had taken up life insurance policies, paid for out of extra few shillings' earnings, these few memorials were added to in after years, for it was a pleasing thought that their names would be read by those who came after – maybe centuries hence. Having read all their favourite epitaphs on the way as they circled the church, and then the one or two notices in the church porch, although they knew them all by heart, the little girls now tiptoed down the cobbled path past the old cross with its broken top, the history of which was an unsolved mystery for no one knew what it represented, shut the gate noiselessly behind them and crept silently until the outer wall was passed – as if they were afraid the sleepers within might be disturbed.

But they were boisterous enough after the little farmhouse where the dreaded bailiff lived and the coachman's cottage – the mistresses of both these houses were elderly and lived in such seclusion that it was really painful to them to have their silence broken by children's noises, and at times in the past they had come out and scolded them vigorously – suddenly the front door would open upon them and the coachman's housekeeper would pounce just like an owl on inoffensive little shrews.

'Whatever's all this Meg's devarsion gooin on?' she would ask. 'I thought it wus a regiement o soljers gooin by or else Old Bonapartie got ere.' Talk of Bonaparte had no doubt been a weapon in her own childhood.

The children would look confounded and kick their shoes together in awed silence.

'Look ow you be a dirtyin on yer stockins!' she would rebuke them crossly. 'Spose you think yer mothers ent got enough to do keeping you tidy weout you makin um uncalled for work – if I was um I'd smack all yer behinds till yer noses bled buttermilk, that I ud, cos if you didn't appen to deserve it today you ud tomorrow. Now off you goo and let me hear no moor on you. Yer mothers want that milk befoor it goos sour (If I knew anything about old Liz Hall she's gen you som a wik ol),' the last utterance under breath and not intended for the children's ears. 'And doon't you come a stampeedin by here no moore.'

So discretion being the better part of valour the children now crept by like mice until they were out of sight if not out of earshot of the ogre, but once they were on the right side of door and window they burst out so loudly that the two Jersey cows and the black donkey, who lived permanently in the field beyond, ran to the hedge and looked over to see what was going on in their quiet world. At the stile where the field path began there was a little more diversion; they would put down their cans and jump backwards and forwards over it, and the boldest ones would walk along the top of the five-barred gate beside it. They would race each other round and round the trees of the little spinney, or pull long vines of convolvulus or wild hops from the hedge and wind them into crowns, bracelets and waistlets to adorn themselves with, for like children of all ages they loved to dress themselves up and pretend they were someone other than they were.

But their favourite place was the stream which ran at the bottom of the first field. Here play began in earnest. Just before they got to it there were two springs which trickled from a bank into a ditch, and it was here that Amy threw away her tea leaves and rinsed the can, for an empty can is a useful utensil with which to play in the brook. Eileen hung back a little because her mother had forbidden her to play near the water, and no matter what Eileen did to disguise the fact, her mother always discovered that her shoes were wet. Amy and Agnes, however, took her usual reluctance for standoffishness and called her a proud stuck-up little minx, afraid of soiling her shoes. 'I tell you what,' said Agnes in a loud whisper. 'We'll keech out some tadpoles and throw them over her.'

Eileen, rather frightened, walked a little way along the bank to where the brook was narrowest, and began to pick some wild honey-suckle growing on the opposite bank. Presently she wandered back to the place where she had left the others. Not a sound came from the place where they had been and Eileen thought rather gladly for she never minded, like the others did, going home alone. She was not at all concerned that they had run off without her while she had been picking honeysuckle. But when she reached the spot, Amy suddenly stood upright and threw a can of water at her, then screamed with laughter at the little victim's frightened squeals and seal-like looks. Then she and Agnes – now rather frightened of what they had done, for hadn't Eileen a mother who might tell their mothers and thus make a whacking inevitable for them? – ran off at top speed.

But the other children were full of sympathy for the bedraggled little girl and Emmie, her special little friend, persuaded her to take off her sodden overall.

'You see, if we spread it out on this bush it'll dry while we have a little play and maybe your mother'll never know. I know: we'll play houses and pretend it's our washing hung out to dry – I think I'll take mine off too for it's a bit wet.' So they all took off their overalls and, not contented with that, washed out their handkerchiefs in the brook and so made a fine show of industry.

They gathered stones from the margin of the cornfield and built their houses which when complete were for all the world like the stone circles of the ancient man which are on Dartmoor and else-where – except that these were square instead of round, and these were furnished too – outlines of stones together with a large spicing of imagination were chairs, tables, sideboards, and there was always a piano on which they played with great hauteur in their idle moments or gave lessons to their little boys and girls.

'I'll get the playpots,' called Sue as she ran off to unearth a collec-tion of broken bits of china which they had hidden on a former occasion. These they divided up with great exactitude between them and began to decorate their houses with them – each fragment was a vase, a cup and saucer, or perhaps a plaque for the wall.

'What are we going to be?' asked Emmie. 'I think I shall be my Aunt Kitty.'

'And I shall be Nelly,' said Eileen. Nelly was a young bride who lived near her mother and was greatly admired by all the children.

'But you must not forget to call me Mrs Follitt for it's rude to say Nelly now I'm married – so mother says. Though it does seem funny when we know she's Nelly all the time, it's like pretending same as when we play.'

'How about you, Sue?' asked Emmie. 'Why don't you be your stepmother, then you can be spiteful to your Ethel?'

But it wasn't in Sue's nature to be spiteful to anyone; besides, she more than the others had need of a brief escape from her real life. So she decided to be Mrs Tomset who had been her own Mother's next door neighbour in happier times.

For the next hour they wore the whole personality of their chosen parts, getting into flusters over poor ovens and cakes that wouldn't come to perfection, waiting rather impatiently for husbands who were a trifle late when dinners were ready to be dished up, or running to the well hurriedly while the baby was asleep and coming back with an imaginary heavy pail in one hand while the other rested on hip, meeting neighbours on the way with whom they exchanged choice snippets of gossip. Every now and then they ran to the bushes and felt the progress of their laundry, and cried in not altogether unreal consternation, 'Dear! Dear! A dreadful day for washing – not a thread dry yet awhile.' And indeed the overalls did seem a very long time in drying.

In the end they saw the men coming home from their work at the farms and wet or dry they hurriedly put them on, collected their precious play pots and hid them in the same usual place, gathered up their milk cans, and made for home like so many Bandersnatchers.

Although the 'Bottom Way' led through a land of enchantment the children rarely made their way home from school by it, but now and then two or perhaps three little girls would suddenly turn aside when they came to the barn where the public notices were displayed upon the door and climbed over the gate, which was always difficult to open, on the opposite side of the road. They always scampered across the first part of Duffus Piece feeling themselves trespassers for no reason at all – unless it were that the scaling of the gate gave them a feeling of breaking in. At the blacksmith's shop they paused, for here they were out of sight to a stray passer-by on the road behind them.

The blacksmith's shop stood dark and silent under overhanging trees, its door nailed up tight, for like the lime kiln, it had not been working for years – hundreds and hundreds the children fancied as they peeped through the blackened and cobwebby window at the anvil and huge bellows lying idle. They had made up a story about the smith and now they almost believed it, that in those dark ages before they were born a giant had come out of the wood behind the shop and spirited him away, no one knew where. At the back of the shop there was a little pond on which a family of moorhens sported themselves, and the little girls delighted in watching their antics, round and round they swam almost turning turtle when they dived into the water after some tempting morsel. The pond was just an overflow of the water which ran from the weir, and just behind it was the Squire's territory with only a dilapidated iron fence dividing that forbidden land from the meadow in which the children were. How dark and mysterious it looked through there with the thick undergrowth and lichen-covered trees, and never a human being in sight. Just within the fence, at the very back of the blacksmith's shop, was a weird and wonderful place like a little cave which the children had been told was an ice house, and very profound discussions they had as to its probable uses. What could this antediluvian place have been used for? In this watery spot multitudes of insects, not to mention frogs and snails, must have abounded – not at all suitable for food supplies. Perhaps it had been the storehouse for iron rations when Bonaparte's army was daily expected.

That part of the meadow was a quagmire, but greatly daring, the children jumped from tuffet to tuffet to gather the Jennygreens, ragged robins, or tall water forget-me-nots which grew dangerously near the pond – what recked they of squelching noises beneath their feet that spelt wet shoes and socks until their hands were full of the coveted flowers? – then perhaps remorse would set in, and they would migrate to the dry and sunny part of the meadow to pick handfuls of cowslips, dandelions or coltsfoot for Mother's wine, hoping thus to placate her should she discover the dampness of their extremities.

'Hark!' cried Betsie suddenly, 'if that ent the horses gooin down to the weir to drink, I never did! Come on I say or us shall be late to tea.'

'And it only seemed a minute or two,' said her sister regretfully.

'Us'll come this way tomorrow – and the next day.' But they didn't, perhaps it would be a year or more before they came that way again.

Reluctantly they left the blacksmith's shop, the ice house, the little moorhens diving and swimming gaily round and round their pond, the rare flowers, and the air of mystery, behind. Over the rickety stile they clambered and were soon pattering along the narrow hard mud path beside the little stream. On the other side of the stream was a strip of woodland, and on the other side of the path a corn field of many acres, and when the corn was grown it towered high above the children's heads so that they were hemmed in on either hand as completely as if they had been walking in a dense forest. Perhaps it was this sense of isolationism which explained why so few of them cared to come this way, for they were mostly children who in after life would grow into those jolly people who love companionship and dislike above all things to be alone. It was only the few who were destined to be solitaries who loved this path.

For a while they hurried on with eyes shut tight to the enticements of the brook; meadowsweet and sweet-smelling water mint grew in abundance, in certain spots watercress, and in clear places little silver fishes, which they tried to catch with their hands, swam to and fro. The wood on the opposite bank held out branches of catkins, pussy willow or honeysuckle, almost but not quite reachable from the side that the children walked on – as if trying to tempt them to come over and play – and usually when they came to the little spinney of pines they could not resist jumping over a narrow place to look for fallen cones, for these were a great novelty – very few if any other pines grew in the neighbourhood. Gone now the resolution to hurry home for the pine wood was too full of enchantment, the soft bed of needles pleasant beneath their feet.

When at last they reached the spot where their path merged into that of the field way, just where the other children had played houses and got their clothes wet, they saw fathers and brothers coming home from work – so to earth they fell with a jerk, which sent them scudding across the last field in the wake of the other children, all intent on being seated decorously around the table when Father came in.

Fathers disport themselves

Fathers only saw their children at their best, leaving home as they did before they were awake and returning to find them seated around the table with freshly washed faces and tidied hair, watching eagerly with shining eyes while Mother served out the gigantic boiled fruit pudding which was always the prelude to their evening meal. Then so intent were they upon appeasing their appetites that even if they had been allowed to talk at table, and they were certainly not, they would not have had any wish to do so. 'Every time you speak you lose a mouthful,' their parents would warn them when first breaking them in to this habit, and these healthy little animals had no desire to do that – at least not on the first course. The savoury course which followed had for its keystone an infinitesimal piece of meat, that usually being boiled bacon, accompanied by a large variety and quantity of vegetables always including potatoes and greens; a meal without these two was unthinkable, but none of the children liked greens and they would push them into a little heap in a secluded spot on their plates, hoping that under cover of their parents' conversation they would not be noticed. Perhaps Mother would absent mindedly say 'Yes' when they asked if they could get down from the table, but it wasn't often that Father was hood-winked, and he would say severely, 'Eat all that's put on your plate first – you'll grow up stunted men and women if you doon't eat greens – or you wunt grow up at all maybe.' They had great faith in the daily intake of greens.

As soon as they were allowed to leave the table they were gone like the wind, each child to his or her own diversion – some playing in the communal games of the hamlet, others wandering around the hedges of nearby fields in a desultory search for something or other, not always to be found, but they were full of expectancy, adventure always lurked in the shadow of the next hedge.

The Fox Inn at Juniper Hill. Betty refers to this inn as 'The Fox and Hounds', and it was also Flora's 'Wagon and Horses'.

So Father had a nice quiet evening, almost oblivious of his progeny after he had done the few 'man's jobs' about the house which his wife had been on about for weeks, such as hammering a nail into something or other, stopping up a hole in her washing pan or big pot, and nearly always tacking a tip or two onto one of the children's shoes. Then he would go forth with his hoe to his allotment. There to the accompaniment of his rhythmic hoeing he would spend a couple of hours in solitary contemplation, smoking the while his one pipe of the day in peace. If funds would allow and he was so minded, he would stroll round by the Fox and Hounds on his way home and sit for half an hour over a half pint of twopenny, and maybe play a game of dominoes. It would be dusk when he got back home where the children were unwillingly in from their play – Mother generally had to go out and call their names before she got them, by dint of coaxing and badgering, into the fold and ready for bed before Father came in. The little girls looked like angels in their long white nightdresses as they came to kiss him goodnight, and even the boys, whom he, having been a boy himself, strongly suspected of duplicity, being tired out now looked altogether innocent of guile. As soon as their heads touched the pillows they were all sound asleep until the morning. Mother must have sighed many a time as she carried down the armful of mending, which must be done before they were ready for school on the following day, and the shoes, which she thought she would not mention to Father yet awhile, worn almost through with skipping. She had tried so hard to drum it into the girls that they must not skip no matter how much 'all the go' the game was just now. And how on Earth was she going to find suitable bits of material for putting new behinds into the boy's knickers – why must they want to climb every tree and hedge they came to? In the morning they would squabble and kick up 'Meg's Diversion' generally before she could get them off to school. Yes, only she knew how naughty and tiresome they could be – these little late Victorian dears were just as full of original sin as any of the children of a later age, the unsound theory that they were cherubs in disguise must have originated with fathers who knew so little of their children.

The Fox and Hounds was a place of high diversion, a no man's land – or more correctly speaking perhaps an every man's land, between home and work, a pleasant suspension between the responsibilities of the two, a place where a man could be his true self without let or hindrance. As he scraped the dirt from his boots on the iron scraper at the door in some miraculous way he shed his usual insignificant personality and became a man of importance – like the children on their walks to and from school – but wasn't he one of the children yesterday?

Inside the door was a high-backed settle running almost the length of the room with its back facing the newcomer, thus forming a passage way between it and the wall so that those entering need not find themselves within the public room if they desired their business to be conducted in private. In that case they just stood and waited behind the settle until they were able to get an audience with the landlord or his wife during their flittings to and fro between the cellar, which was really a long flag-stoned kitchen and held two or three barrels of beer on a low form at one end, and the public room.

These unorthodox customers were often treated with short shrift and told to come again next morning when business would not be so brisk for whatever they required, especially if it were soap, soda, starch, or some such fiddle fad. These, with a few other items, were kept by the landlord's wife in the cellar as a sideline – not from any hope of financial gain but she knew full well the propensity of the hamlet women to find themselves short of such commodities on wash day morn, and she was an understanding woman. Well, let them wait until the morning for them, besides, she had a good idea that, coming at that time in the evening, what they really wanted was to hear what was going on behind the settle. Now if it were a piece of cheese wanted for Father to take for his bavor next day it would be a different matter, she would hastily hew a chunk from their own stock in trade and waste no words about it.

But for the authentic client there was ever a warm welcome even though the amount of hard cash he would spend was likely to be infinitesimal, for was he not part of the heart and pulse of that pleasant glowing atmosphere, contributing as he did his quota of warmth and goodwill, cheerfulness and wisdom for the benefit of all?

If the evening was still young, perhaps he would find himself first of the company to arrive; then he would sit scarcely sipping his beer, for he had to make it last during the whole of his stay, and exchanging laconic comments with the landlord and his wife who sat in the kitchen eating their evening meal before the hustle and bustle of the evening began in real earnest. Or, if another was there before him, the two would sit at either end of the settle and carry on a heart-to-heart conversation about the world in general and their own portion of it in particular, or they would draw up a table and play solemn games of dominoes. But it was not long before another and another dropped in with a hearty, 'Watcher Harry, Watcher Tom. You doon't mean to say you two be let loose, do ee, begoy.'

'Ah-h, that us be, it ud take a strong leash to keep chaps like us tethered, udn't it, Tom?'

'That it ud. Us bean't them duffers they grows over at Imly, be us Harry? Let's see, wordn't you born thereabouts, Jack?'

'That I wer – and a very good job they made on it I must say though I bean't a bostful chap.'

'Ah-h, come to think on it I did see a shabby fellow we a trumpet goo by tother day, he said he'd ad the sack – chap was gooin to blow for imself to further orders.'

Before the merriment caused by this sally had subsided, the door opened again and a young soldier home on furlough came round the settle. His scarlet coat gleamed against the dark walls of the taproom giving a touch of brilliance and excitement to the scene. Several other men came upon his heel and when all had taken seats, theirs by rights of custom, and had exchanged the usual pleasantries with those already assembled, the conversation centred on the young soldier. Only a few short weeks ago he had been an unconsidered hobbledehoy who had found farm work not altogether to his liking and had grown tired of the restricting atmosphere of his home, filled to overflowing as it was with younger brothers and sisters, and perhaps the least bit tired too of his mother's pandering – so he had taken the only outlet, that of soldiering.

Now he called for his pint, one for his father and another for their next door neighbour who had accompanied them, with a sophisticated man-of-the world air. He also, for the first time, began to call the older men by their Christian names in a most matter-of-fact manner whereas, being an underling, previously he had addressed them as Master this and that. Now here was a miracle, a scarlet coat had turned him into a fully fledged man overnight, or nearly so. Not all the khaki tunics which were to be worn in the years that followed had the power to do this – in fact they often had the reverse effect on their young wearers, making them appear so pitiably boyish.

'Now I spose you knows about all they can larn you about soldiering, Sammy, or they udn't a sent you hum so quick?' asked one.

'I picked up a lot on it meself weout any learning,' Sammy grinned. 'I knows how to be smart at the cookhouse door so that I gets a good dollop of dinner.'

'That's the style, me lad, a belly well lined is half the battle, that it is.'

'Ther's moor to it nor that, me buoy, think about the honner an glory you wins by fightin for yer Queen and country.'

'What about when there's no wars to fight in? Then Tommy Atkins is all out o date – a lazy, good for nothing young gallus! According to folkses' talk.'

'But ther is a gooin to be a war now midlin soon, doon't spose you've eared about the way them Boers be a carrying on, Queen sais she can't stand much moor on it – though doon't ee goo telllin folks I told ee.' Sammy gave out this piece of news in a low voice with the air of one telling a state secret.

A moment's silence followed this bombshell, then one man said sarcastically, 'I spose Colonel told ee? Come on, Sammy, he sez sez ee, Goo and say good bye to your mother then you an me ull goo off to Africee an settle them there Boers.'

Most of the men laughed and the boy, flushed like a peony, said modestly, 'It's all the talk at Aldershot anyhow.'

'Ther wun't be no more wars as long as the world stands, nothing surer nor that,' said another man bringing his fist down heavily upon the table to emphasise his conviction.

'No! No!' agreed some of the others. 'Them old savage days be done we.'

'I'm not so sure,' said another quietly. 'I read in the newspaper that there old Kruger's rearing up uncommonly – a regular old nitre he seems to be by all accounts.'

'He'd better sing low,' said one who had lately come back to his native village after serving twenty-one years in the army. 'Why, our chaps ud wipe out the lot on em in a week, look at them gret big guns us a got.'

The conversation for the next half hour was all about this rumour of war which would surely never come now that the world was so civilised – but come it did, and for the exception of the few years between the end of it and the beginning of the 1914 war, peace was never more to be the background of their lives. Now they debated its management and mismanagement like true armchair philosophers; most of their views were absurd and childlike in the extreme – but not so much so as those of some of the politicians of today. Just as they were getting really heated Mr Moore stepped in, and as he had no taste for such serious matters, he broke up the discussion by twiddling the strings of his banjo and singing one of his ridiculous songs and thus created a lighter atmosphere. Other of the company were asked to oblige with a song, but most of them were too reserved to make themselves so conspicuous, although none minded joining in the choruses.

'What about you, Colonel Crampoirn?' asked Mr Moore of the young soldier. (Who the original Colonel Crampoirn was no one ever seemed to have the slightest idea, but his name was freely used in addressing anyone who was dressed up or had a slight swagger.)

The boy blushed shyly but got to his feet and sang in a pleasant voice a song, which was new to the company, which he had heard in Aldershot and indeed was being sung with great gusto everywhere at that time: 'We don't want to fight. But by jingo if we do! We've got the ships, we've got the men, we've got the money too.' Those who were quick at picking up a tune were with him in the second verse, and towards the end even those with no voice at all were humming – rather like bees accidentally trapped in a honey pot it is true, but with feelings as fervid as those of the more articulate ones. The good old English lion wasn't going mangy yet awhile, in fancy they wiped the ground with those damned Boers.

After such a stirring up they would have liked to have had their pots replenished and one or two recklessly did so, but the wiser ones refrained knowing full well that money can't be spent twice, for as Tom Ayres remarked to his neighbour, 'T'is like Dick's hatband – it wun't goo round twice and tie – if you wants a bit of a bow to smarten up we like you've got to be satisfied we once round.'

'Ah-h! Ah-h! you be right there, Tom, that you be,' agreed the others.

The thriftless ones would fain have asked the landlord's credit until their next ship came in, but there was his answer in black and white, framed and glazed, over the fireplace: 'Since man to man was so unjust, no man can tell what man to trust. I've trusted many to my sorrow, so pay today and I'll trust tomorrow.' And what would be more adamant than the printed word, it carries more weight than all the oral argument in the world – and carries no personal offence.

Was it that night or the night after, or maybe some weeks hence, that a stranger drew up at the gateway and getting down from the trap in which he rode, tied his sturdy little cob to the iron palings and himself walked up the pathway carrying a strange and unwieldy object which he deposited upon the taproom table with a self-congratulatory air? All looked askance and the landlord who had just come in to make up the fire said shortly, 'What have you got there?' in a tone of voice that plainly said, 'If it's any funny business you're up to you'll get short shrift here.' It might be some new sort of cannon ball for all he knew, all this talk of war made him feel uneasy. But the stranger only smiled cryptically as he uncovered that object and then stepped back a little better to see the full effect of the revelation upon the company. 'It's a Talking Machine,' he announced triumphantly. If he had let a crocodile loose it wouldn't have caused more amazement.

Nor would their approach have been any different. They were a cautious race and accepted nothing on trust. But in this case seeing and hearing was believing, for after a prolonged delay while the owner of this marvel, who was himself a novice, put on the cylinder and set the complicated machinery going, a whole volley of hissings and grating sounds came forth in which a voice was mingled sure enough – a strange voice indeed which might have belonged to a visitant from Mars or the Moon, but a human voice without a doubt, and when it got going thoroughly the words were quite distinguishable – at least to those who were quick on the uptake. What were they now? An ultra-modern popular song? Or perhaps a snatch from one of Gilbert and Sullivan's operas? Whatever it was, depend upon it, that was the last word in musical entertainment for the next several years, ousting from favour all the 'Ta Ras', 'Maggy Murphies', 'Girls with Golden Hair' and the naughty irresistible 'Flo', hitherto still fondly cherished in this corner, although long out of favour in the rest of the world.

The reactions of the audience were varied but all were deeply impressed in one way or another. 'Lawk Amassey!' said some and withdrew within themselves to think it over.

'It's be in the newspapers, all about it,' said Sam the roadman. 'But there I thought it wer only a lot o tackle to fill um up we like – never dreampt it wer the truth, that I never did.'

'It's gooin agen God Almighty, that's what I call it,' said Tom Watts solemnly.

'Hundreds and thousands on um about,' said the 'scientist', who didn't like to be caught behindhand in anything. 'Why our Lizzie's young man's mother's had one for the last year – only it's a lot bigger nor this so it talks moor.'

'Spose they be mighty dear, Mister, bean't um?' asked Jim Wells diffidently. 'I should just about like to have one for my old Mum, who never gets out wat we her bad leg and our house being miles from the next – it ud just about be company for her I'll bet.'

'Well, I got this one for a song as you might say from one of the young gents in Oxford yesterday – they always want to have all the latest contraptions – not thinking to count the money in their trousers pocket first like poorer folk do, so they get into debt and have to part with their toys to pay the piper something off, or else they get tired of them and fling them away like children do when they've got too many toys to be good for them. My sister has a boarding house for some of them who don't live in the colleges, and this was one of her young gents – a nice feller if there ever was one, full of nonsense but could talk well, he could talk a sittie hen off her nest, so when he said, 'Mr Tapper, I believe you want a Talking Machine, and I want a golden sovereign,' I said that was just what I wanted, although I hadn't thought a word about such a thing till that minute. So when I was coming along the turnpike, I thought to myself I'll drop into the Fox and Hounds and give the Landlord and his company the biggest suprise of their lives, for I lay they never heard one of these before, no never heard of them I don't suppose.' The landlord, backed by a chorus of grunts and murmurs from the company, thanked the stranger for his civility as he carefully covered up the magical box and prepared to take his leave. A dead silence followed his exit. Here was something beyond words. Time had flown relentlessly during this rich entertainment, it was already dusk and some of them had an uneasy feeling that their wives would be reproaching them for overstaying when they got home; and one or two of whom it was said that the 'Missis wore the breeches' in their houses, in order to placate them, asked the landlord to put half a pint of porter in a bottle – thus mortgaging his own half pint for another evening.

But the women were so amazed on hearing the news of the Talking Machine that they too were almost speechless. 'W-a-a-l! W-a-a-l! Whatever be us comin to?' most of them gasped. Tis true Rose Rouse turned on Tom and accused him of being a bit tiddley and seeing and hearing double. 'What! on half a pint of threepenny?' demanded the aggrieved Tom. 'It ent quite so strong as all that though it is middlin tackle.'

And mothers take their ease

Although Mrs Timson despised village gossip and, like her house, turned her back upon it, she did not disdain to receive any unit of the community who sought whatever help or advice she had to give, or who wanted to pour their secret sorrows or joys into a sympathetic ear in her own cottage – that is, in the early afternoon when she had everything in apple pie order, the children were not yet due home from school, and her husband well away at his work for some hours to come. In the morning she would bear no intrusion and would almost sweep a persistent caller off the doorway with her brisk broom. If anyone delayed their going unduly, she would politely but firmly bid them adieu by saying, 'I have a pudding to make now so must be getting on with it or my husband's meal won't be ready when he comes in, and that will never do.' While saying this she had piloted the dallying visitor onto the doorstep.

A footstep on the pathway behind the cottage heralded a caller and she would drop her sewing or book and look up expectantly wondering who it might be – it was almost tantalising to hear people coming without being able to see them and almost always disappointing when they did materialise, for that ideal person whom everyone is always expecting almost never seems to arrive. If the door was open, and it usually was, she could see who it was before they had time to knock, reflected in a large picture which hung opposite the door. It was only young Mrs Pollitt with the sixpenny worth of eggs she had asked for yesterday – a round dozen in a dainty basket made out of the last summer's chip straw hat and lined with blue sateen.

'How natty you are, Nelly my dear!' exclaimed Mrs Timson, examining the basket which was very much after her own heart. 'You ought to have a little shop and sell such things.'

'But who's going to buy them?' asked Nelly ruefully. 'Nobody passes our window in a month of Sundays, besides men going to work on the allotments and I'm sure they ent likely to buy such things.'

'Oh well, of course you'd have to get a house round in the front street.'

'I shouldn't like that, it's so noisy round there, and I couldn't abear to live so public either.'

'That is so of course,' agreed Mrs Timson. 'But I do wish there was a shop in the place, it would make it so much more important.'

'I'm going to have a sewing machine,' blurted Nelly, who had been dying to let out this bit of news and had really brought the eggs just then to give her an opportunity. 'It's a real beauty, the very latest, it's coming from Singer's, the man's just been, and I paid him the five shillings down and Charlie's going to pay the shilling a week out of his pocket. Mr Singer is going to send it next week and they will show me how to work it.'

'Well I never!' Mrs Timson was thoroughly interested. 'I don't think we've ever had a sewing machine come into the place before. You will be able to do a bit of dressmaking for folks.'

'Yes, and I'll do all your long seams in nightgowns and things for nothing that I will, you'll only have to mention it when you want anything done.'

'That's very good natured, and it will be a real Godsend to me. But you are not going to make a fortune if you go on like that.'

Nor did she. By the time she had redeemed her promise to Mrs Timson, turned all her mother's sheets sides into the middle and made batches of underwear for each of her unmarried sisters and sister-in-law, she had little enough time for her own clothes; and if she did sometimes make a child's frock or a blouse for an outsider she was far too generous to charge for it, besides, nobody in the hamlet had ever been known to charge for anything they did for anyone else, all good deeds were pooled – a sort of banking account they might be glad to draw upon themselves on some distant rainy day.

However, this pioneer of sewing machines had far reaching results – indirectly it was responsible for a revolution in the dress of the female population of the hamlet who had hitherto been content with the fashions of twenty or more years before. Now seeing the wonderful achievements of this one, three or four other women were tempted to buy machines and, with this royal road before them, set out to make their own and their children's clothes. Materials were so cheap in those days that even they could afford a length sometimes for a blouse or a dress and a fashion book with at least one free pattern could be bought in town for a penny when a suitable one could not be borrowed, and although most of them confessed to being a bit flummoxed when it came to cutting out, there was always some kind friend a bit handier with her scissors ready and willing to undertake that critical operation. So it happened that sometimes one of Mrs Timson's afternoon callers would be upon this errand bent.

'Oh, do ee mind helping me to cut out this blouse?' a wistful voice would say. 'I've a bin starin at this pattern till my head aches like a turnup, and I can not make heads nor tails on it, that I can't. For one thing there's only one sleeve, they must a forgot to put tother un in. And I did want to get it done be Sunday for us be all gooin over to our Mother's birthday and I know my two sisters ull be there dressed up to the nines and I doon't want them to think I be all behind the fair – if I be married and done for as the saying goos.'

'May as well be out of the world as out of the fashion,' remarked the 'friend in time of need' brightly, as she spread the piece of flowered cotton stuff with its satin stripe – very like the wall paper of the period – out on the table and began to lay the pattern on it. For the next half hour she was in her element cutting and pinning up the blouse.

Or it might be someone with a hat to be trimmed, although there was not as much demand for this service as in the past, for now that women were beginning to get about on bicycles, they saw for themselves that plainer hats were being worn in the world at large. They were not slow to adopt a plain ribbon bow for the hat that had previously carried enough flowers to dress a Maygarland, not to mention a few feathers and odd bits of veiling. However, a bow needed to be made nicely and put on at the correct angle, now that they had suddenly become so clothes conscious, and they were not all born milliners.

'Now this colour won't go at all well with your dress, you can't wear two bright colours like those together, unless you want to look like a horse at a flower show! Perhaps I can find a bit that would look better.' And out would come a cardboard box filled with ribbons and laces sent by a kind aunt for the children to dress their dolls, but used for no such wasteful purpose. There was a great deal of trying on in front of the little mirror before both wearer and milliner were altogether satisfied with the result – the hat might have been intended for the Chelsea garden party, at least.

But more often than not it was a letter that needed writing, for there were old ones about who had received no schooling, and even the middle-aged and older young who, although well able to write to members of their family, rarely felt competent to answer a letter which came from outside the family circle. These epistles were mostly between mothers of young daughters and their mistresses either applying for posts or giving notice to quit. Sometimes, but very rarely, of more serious portent.

'Will ee write me a letter, there's a good soul? I be that worritted I can't sit down.'

'Oh come! I never before heard of worry striking at that part of the body.'

'Well you knows what I mean – I can't settle to do nothing like, I be that mommered.'

'Well I'll make you a good strong cup of tea – the kettle is hot on the hob, it won't take a minute to come to the boil, and that will clear your head a bit. Now what is it all about?'

Poor Mrs Ayres ran her hands through her greying hair, pushing her hat on top of it to a most comical angle as she subsided into the nearest chair. 'It's this,' she explained holding out a letter. 'It's from our young Rose; she says her Missis has lost two rings and she seems to think our young Rose as ad um, and you know yerself our young Rose udn't do anything like that, I brought my chuldern up to be honest every jack one on um, I never let um take a pin that wasn't their own by rights.'

'Oh I see,' said Mrs Timson who was reading through the letter, 'Rose is upsetting herself about it – thinks she will perhaps have to go to prison! They will have to prove that she took them before that and I don't somehow think they will be able to do it, as you say Rose wouldn't steal anybody's rings or anything else. She has been in her place three years now, hasn't she? Well, her mistress must know by now what sort of girl she is, surely. Perhaps Rose only fancies that they suspect her – after all she had not been accused according to the letter. No doubt the lady is overwrought about losing her valuable jewels and that makes her a bit snappish with Rose, and she takes it to heart, poor girl! Well its quite understandable on both sides when you come to think about it. The best thing to my way of thinking is to have no rings, then you're not worried by loosing them. Well, I'll write a few lines to the mistress if you want me to.'

And so it was a letter addressed in Mrs Timson's beautiful Italian script was laid upon a London breakfast table next morning and presently Rose was called into the room, a few tears were shed and all was forgiven and forgotten between mistress and maid. Rose had never been suspected, and the rings were eventually found.

But not all the daughters of the hamlet were as innocent of guile as Rose, and the letters from their disillusioned mistresses were by no means easy to answer – the soft answer had no power to turn away their righteous indignation and often the erring one would follow bag and baggage close upon the heels of the postman, for it was 'one toot and you'r oot' with servant girls in those days, when there was no dearth of them in the land.

One day the fat woman who had danced with Eileen came to the door, her bland face was somewhat clouded by a look of anxiety, not unmixed by a tinge of pleasurable anticipation.

'I know what a beautiful writer you be, my dear,' she began in her cajoling voice, 'and if you ull be so kind, my dear, as to answer this one for me I shall be that glad, that I shall. Well! I've never bin in your house before,' as she was asked to step inside. 'My! ent you got it nice an snug.'

'Too snug to my way of thinking,' replied Mrs Timson in a slightly acid voice, for it was the greatest bugbear of her life that she had so little space in which to live and move. 'I don't have everybody popping in and out at all times – so you're not the only one who hasn't been inside my door before, although I've lived here more than twenty years. Yes, I shall be pleased to write a letter for you if you want me to. What is it about?'

'Well, this come from some place a bit away from here; it's about our Joe, I ent sin him this thirty year, that I ent, and now it seems he's dead – an he's lef a bit o money, an it seems that I bein his only sister left alive ought to come in for it. I wish you'd write and ask um to send it on as soon as they can, and when it comes I shall buy you a pound of the very best tea in the shops my dear, that I shall.'

The letter was from the farmer for whom the poor old man had worked. He had gone without proper food and warmth and all the little things that make life bearable to scratch and save these few paltry pounds, and now they would be gone like a shower of rain.

Or one day perhaps, following the heralding footsteps on the invisible pathway, a figure not unlike that of Mrs Noah from a child's Noah's ark would be reflected and transposed upon the picture of the lady in the elegant pink dress, who sauntered through the flowery woodland fondly caressing with her hand the life-sized St Bernard who walked beside her, while he, with kindly condescension, looked at the little white dog, no bigger than his foot, who gambled before them. Mrs Polly Trimble was dressed for the occasion, she had put on a clean blouse and her good black tail – as skirts were called – which reached to the ground all round and completely hid her boots, making her look as if she was solid from the waist downwards. A wide petersham belt with a silver buckle as large as a breast plate allied blouse and shirt and a lone silver chain about her neck with watch tucked into the belt completed the ensemble. She had washed quite a lot of the snuff from her face but now that face, alas! wore a look of woe. She sat down on the nearest chair without saying a word, took out her snuff box and offered it to her hostess who, to show there was no ill feeling took a pinch – although she greatly despised snuff taking for it was now considered a dirty habit and only indulged in by Polly and one other old lady in the hamlet – but after a moment under the pretext of moving the kettle she threw it on the fire and then, not to hurt her guest's feelings, sat down and sniffed her empty fingers.

'You could have knocked me down with a feather and that's the mortal truth!' said Polly feelingly when at last she emerged from her snuff-produced reverie.

Her hostess waited patiently for further enlightenment, hoping in her heart that the matter had some relation to Polly's past which was a closed book to most and therefore of absorbing interest, although she had been permitted to peep at a few lines here and there – the headings of chapters as it were, which had only given her a thirst to read more deeply.

'Yes, a feather would have knocked me down. Little did I think to run into anybody who knew me from bygone times after all these years.'

'How did it all come about?' asked Mrs Timson, trying to keep too much interest from her voice.

'It was like this, you know what a nice day it was Monday? Well, I felt as fresh as a daisy so when Sam had gone to work, I thought it would do no harm if I went to town and got me a few bits of shopping – a bit of barm to work a drop of elderberry wine, and so on. So I dressed meself in me best bib and tucker, put on the gold earings and necklaces that belonged to me Aunt Bucket – I felt sorry afterwards that I had decked meself so, for he might not have recognized me in everyday clothes, for I was a smart little piece in the byegone, although I say it meself. I don't know if it was the nice day or what it was that made me do it but when I passed the brewery I all at once thought to meself I'd go in and order a little tiddly nine gallon barrel of beer to come by the carrier, for it would save Sam going round the Fox and Hounds on dark nights; besides, it would be handy if I fancied a drop meself when I didn't feel very grand. It comes cheaper by the barrel too than by giving twopence ha'penny a pint, not to mention the shoe leather you wear out fetching it.'

'I should think it would be dearer myself', suggested the listener, 'for it would be gone sooner.'

'Well, of course that's neither here nor there,' replied Polly evasively. 'Anyway, I went in, there was a man talking very deedy to the clerk but he stepped aside while I give me order and address to have it sent to, and paid down the ten shillings it cost – two wagon wheels I'd saved up for a good while and meant to keep a good while longer, but thinks I to meself, may as well joy ourselves while we're alive, what's the use of five shilling bits when we're dead?'

'None whatever!' agreed Mrs Timson. 'Well? So far so good. What happened after that?'

'A knock came at my door this morning and when I opened it there stood a man all dressed up to the nines smiling like a Cheshire cat – somehow, although I'd scarcely glanced at him at the time, I recognised him to be the man who was talking to the clerk at the brewery the other day. 'Good morning, Mrs Kingham that was,' said he, all bowing and scraping. 'Ah ah! You see somebody remembers you from the old Rose and Crown days – let's see, how long ago was it? Twenty-odd years. Well well, time flies, as the monkey said when he threw the clock out of the window. Here's my card.'

'Mr Harman. Representing Pascoe's Brewery. Shirehampton.' 'Yes. John, my first husband had dealt there when he kept the Rose and Crown. I couldn't remember the name of Harman though for a bit, but after I'd cast back in my memory it came to me pat – Tom Harman, he'd been a pot man for John. He was there when John died. I don't think I'm far wrong in saying a lot must have stuck to his fingers for never having had any head for business, I had to leave things to his management until the brewery sold me up.'

'You seem to have got on since then,' I said. 'But what is your business with me today, may I ask? I don't want to order anything for I got me little nine gallon cask from Goodmayes Brewery only this last week.'

'I was there on business when you came in to order it and so discovered your present whereabouts. The long and short of it is you still owe some money to Pascoes, but we have never been able to get in touch with you until now. I've got to collect that money and should thank you paying at least part of it now.'

'I hope you didn't pay it,' said Mrs Timson. 'Even if you did owe it at the time they can't make you pay it now, it's too long ago. Besides, there seems to me to be something underhanded about this Harman.'

'I told him I hadn't got any money, I should have to ask Sam for it – that seemed quite feasible although it wasn't the truth, but I didn't want him to see me take down the pewter teapot where I keep it – though none but you and me know that. So he said he'd call again next week when I was to be sure and have it ready or else there'd be the devil to pay.'

'Well, you don't want to pay two devils. Haven't you got any papers telling what happened and what didn't when they sold you up after John's death – you ought to have kept receipts for all you paid away – oh, you have got something I see,' as Polly opened an antiquated leather handbag and brought forth a small bundle of faded papers. 'We may learn something from these.'

But they turned out to be only a few letters and bills gathered up haphazardly from a desk before it was sold, nothing to help to solve the present quandary. Some of the letters, however did throw new light on the past and so whetted Mrs Timson's curiosity to know still more. After assuring Polly that no power on Earth could compel her to pay any money owing or not owing as the case might be, for more than twenty years, and suggesting that a letter to the 'Fountain Head' of the brewery would be the thing and not deal with a mere minion like Harman, with a few diplomatic promptings she led her 'client' on to tell the story of her life.

Good solid middle class, the Buckets had been, born to a substantial income and surrounded by massive mahogany furniture, immense dinner services the tureens of which could have hidden Ali Baba and his forty thieves, or at least some of them, a good well-stacked linen press, fine damask and plush hangings and all such like things that added to their dignity and made them enviable to those just below them on the social ladder.

Grandfather Bucket ruled his house and family with a rod of iron. His meek little wife regarded each word that fell from his lips as a pearl of wisdom. He ruled the roost entirely. They had no sons but he was careful to educate their two daughters as became their position. Caroline, the elder of the two, inherited most of her mother's meekness and grew up according to her father's plan but Emma, the younger, was unlike either parent, wilful, disobedient and prone to gaiety – which she had little chance of enjoying. She must have been a throwback to a former generation. Soon after she came home from the select boarding school where her parents had dutifully sent her to be 'finished', she ran off with a young man of no account, thus finishing herself as far as her family was concerned; her ancestral home was for ever closed to her, and she and the young man whom she had chosen, disappeared into the void.

As the years passed first the mother and later the father died. Caroline was in sole and solitary possession of the solid house and its comfortable furnishings, when one day the door bell rang timidly, and the door being opened there on the step stood a shy little girl in a dropping crinoline dress, long drawers, the lace bottoms of which were somewhat wilted, elastic sided boots, and a little pork pie hat perched on her flaxen-haired head; a small valise was clutched in one hand and a letter in the other. A pathetic little figure.

The woman servant eyed her up and down feeling certain there was something familiar about her which she couldn't for the life of her place.

'Well. Who are you? And what do you want, my dear?' she asked with gruff kindness.

'I'm Mary Ann,' replied the child tremulously. 'My Mother told me to come here because her sister lives in this house, and I have brought a letter for her, if you will please give it to Miss Caroline Bucket who is my aunt; she will understand, my Mother said.'

'Well! Well! Well! Did you ever?' gasped Kezie. 'This is a surprise and no mistake. You had better come in, and sit on this chair while I go and find the mistress.'

The child sat stiffly on the chair, the gaze of her pale blue eyes fixed upon the opposite wall, vaguely wondering what was to happen next in her raggle-taggle world which hitherto had held nothing but insecurity, in which her parents, inadequate as they were, had been some slight support; now deserted by them, all alone, such a small stranger in a strange county, her world seemed to be shattered to smithereens.

She had been sitting there for hours and hours – so it seemed to her although it was barely ten minutes – when the servant returned with a lady who somehow resembled her mother, which was strange because instead of her mother's bright dark eyes and black ringlets she had a mousey complexion and almost colourless hair, but she had a soft kind voice which at once gave hope and assurance to the little five-year-old.

'So you are Mary Ann?' she asked cheerfully as she lifted her to her feet upon the chair, that she might examine her features the better. 'I shall call you Polly, it is a far prettier name, besides, as you are going to be my own little girl, it is only right that I should name you as I wish.' So she proclaimed her proprietorship over the child. 'Now now, no tears,' for Polly finding herself so close to such a kind shoulder had hidden her face against it and burst into tears. 'We shall take care of you, Kezia and I. Kezia will do all manner of things to make you happy – won't you Kezie?'

'That will I do, Miss Carrie, and that right willingly for she's the very spit of you when you were her age – the minute I set eyes on her I said to meself, "Now where on earth have I seen this little gal before for seen her I surely have or my name isn't what it is?" I think the foremost thing is to get her something to eat and that I'll set about doing right now for the poor little maid must be famishing after her journeying.'

'I'll go out shopping first thing tomorrow and get her a few decent clothes,' said Miss Bucket.

'That's right, that's right, you do so,' replied the unceremonious Kezie. 'Or folks might think she's come to us from a circus in that finery.'

So it was that Polly was brought up by her Aunt Bucket and the faithful Kezia. She was rather a dull child, slow on the uptake, with none of the gaiety and – for which her guardians thanked God – none of the selfish wilfulness of her mother; and although weak willed and easily influenced by anyone nigh her, she had many good homely qualities which endeared her to the two women who watched over and cared for her as a tender plant all through her childhood and early youth. Her parents were never heard of again; according to Emma's letter to her sister they were flying abroad in haste to escape the results of some folly they had committed, which was why, she said, they must abandon the child.

When Miss Bucket died suddenly at the age of fifty, Polly was nineteen in years but far younger in her knowledge of the world, such a sheltered life had she led. Kezia was no longer a staff to lean on for she was now past seventy and going downhill fast in both body and mind. So here was Polly, a mere child quite unfitted to steer her own course through the rocks and shallows of life.

The house was hers and a small fortune, which in the hands of a capable woman had been modest riches, but in those of a thriftless young girl, just melted away like butter in the sun. She soon made new friends, some of whom could have been little to her Aunt's liking, and they were ever ready with advice, the acceptance of which, and she hadn't the moral courage to decline it, nearly always left her poorer though a little wiser. In a few short years her inheritance had almost melted away; a mere hundred or two left in the bank plus the house and its furnishings were all that remained. She could not go on for much longer spending money willy nilly, and directly it became apparent that her resources were dwindling to nothingness, her 'friends' began to fall off.

Just then a man twenty years her senior persuaded her to marry him. She did not know, and never did, much about him except that he had got through a considerable fortune of his own. He had lived a gay life but now was prepared to settle down with his little brown hen of a bride: he would even work if necessary and when, after marriage, her resources were found to be at very low ebb – not nearly as flourishing as he had hoped – he had the brilliant idea of gathering all she had together and investing it in an inn which was vacant in a small but thriving market town some distance away. A man was engaged to serve in the bar and a woman servant for the market dinners which were a noted feature of the place. So John had but to act the host, a part he filled most successfully for had he not the air of a man of the world which goes down so well with the clientele of an inn? Nor did he expect his wife to soil her hands, she should sit in the parlour clad in her silks and satins and read her novelettes to her heart's content.

All went well apparently for several years but there all the time was the canker eating at the core of the business – John had a weakness for drink and in such close quarters with it the habit became a disease and things were left too much in the hands of the barman and servant woman, neither of whom were scrupulously honest, for Polly continued to sit in the parlour reading, doing a little tatting and sipping port wine until her head and understanding were more addled than ever. She was almost oblivious of all that was going on around her.

Even in his more sober days John had been most nonchalant in money matters, letting his clients run up debts without so much as asking 'can you? will you? pay', for what was the loss of a little money compared with being thought of as a 'good fellow'. He kept the best house in the town, they said, and on market and fair days the long dining room was filled to capacity with farmers and business men, the huge rounds of beef and unbelievably immense puddings melted away like butter in the sun. Some of the diners were mean enough, under cover of the hubbub of conversation, to go out without paying their footing. Fanny Daw, the serving woman, and Tom Sharman were well aware of this but they knew they were likely to find a silver sixpence under certain plates instead of the twopences which were the usual tips in those days, and sixpence was sixpence. 'If you mean to get on in the world you can't afford to turn money away when it's offered you,' they would tell each other. So they turned a blind eye and a deaf ear on that and many other things which in time caused the downfall of the house. Finances became more and more strained until the day came when the brewer's bill could not be met. Things dragged on for a time, the cellar was not so well stocked, customers began to take away their patronage – at least the honest ones did. John drank more and more heavily and died suddenly in an attack of delirium tremens.

Polly was distracted but didn't know what to do; she had no more initiative than had the little girl who had long years before stood on her aunt's doorstep – and she felt just as forlorn. From her birth onwards she had been a pawn of other people, never being allowed her own individuality, for even her kind aunt in her day had entirely dominated her. She had many good qualities which had never been allowed to flower. Now here she was alone in a situation that would have quailed a much stouter heart than hers.

* * *

'Dear dear! So that is how it all came about,' remarked the listener sympathetically as the teller of the tale paused to take breath and another pinch of snuff. She had always longed to hear this story but now felt slightly disappointed that it wasn't a more romantic one, but there, who would have thought of Polly as a figure for romance? 'So they sold you up lock, stock, and barrel as the saying goes?' she prompted.

'Everything. All the beautiful furniture that came from Aunt Bucket – T'was a heart breaking affair I can tell you. I'm not saying that I hadn't got a few things tucked away in my boxes with my clothes, and they left me my bed and a table and chair, because that's the law.'

'That would be the gate-legged table that I've always admired so, and that tall-backed chair with the crimson damask cover, I'll be bound?'

'Yes. And there were little damask curtains to the bed but I cut them up straight away to make bits of curtains for the windows, seeing that they were bare except for short blinds – I thought all the neighbours would be peeping in when the lamp was alight.'

'So they would, bless you, seeing how full of curiosity folks are. But dear me, how must you have missed all your little comforts coming to such a poor place. I always wondered how you got in touch with Sam – I should dearly like to know – it shall go no farther that, I promise you.'

'I don't know that I would mind you knowing now that you know all the rest. It was old Sam mind you, no doubt you've heard that, though it was before your time. Well, old Sam had a donkey cart in them days and he used to do a bit of carting and shopping for folks round about. He had come into town, and being told by somebody or other about our sale, he thought he might likely pick up a bed cheap for young Sam who was always grumbling about his – and well he might, believe me, for it was all to bits.

'The auctioneer's men had put all my bits of things together in the parlour so that they shouldn't be mixed up with the things they were going to sell; they put a ticket on the door with Private on it and told me to keep the door locked if I liked to. So there I sat listening to folks coming and going to the dining room where the sale was going on. I felt very low for I didn't know what was going to become of me, I hadn't a friend or relation in the world and I had got to get somewhere to go that night or next morning at best. I didn't know where to look, there was nobody in the town who would take me for folks were that spiteful against a person who went bankrupt thenadays as if they had committed a terrible crime, even though they weren't owed anything themselves. I should have to find some work but what and how I didn't dare to think for although I was then past forty I had scarcely had to soil my hands, never having been called upon to do more than a few little fiddling jobs, so what use would I be? I almost wished the world would open up and swallow me up, that I did. I'd shed buckets full of tears and I don't know that they'd eased me at all. I tried to plan what to do, but my brain felt benumbed so I gave up and hoped that the dear Lord would provide for me in some way. I went out to the kitchen and made me a cup of good strong tea and when I was back in the parlour drinking it the door burst open – for I'd forgotten to turn the key, and in comes a man with black whiskers and fierce black eyes.

'We looked one another up and down for a minute. "If you're wanting the sale I said it's in the long room at the bottom of the passage. Nobody's supposed to come in here. Didn't you read the notice on the door saying so?"

'"That I never did, and so a good reason too – I can't read, Missis."

'Then he eyed my boxes all corded up and asked me if I wanted to go anywhere.

'"Because if you do, Missis, I'll take ee and welcome – I be a sort of a carrier in a way and my old moke and cart be standing outside waitin for a job."

'He had a kind voice and it went to my heart. Before I knew where I was I told him I'd nowhere to go and nobody to look to.

'"Come blow me buttons," he said. "If that ent a pretty tidy fix to be in." Just at that minute somebody came in to speak to me about something or other and he went out, course I thought I'd see the last of him but later on he came back.

' "I bin a thinkin, Missis, about what you said when I come in here befoor, and doon't you go and take offence at what I be a gooin to say to you. Wa-al, it's like this, I bin a lookin for a housekeeper this last couple o years – a decent body as ud look after me an my son. It's a poor place – and I can see you be used to things better, but you can do whatever you like we it, drape it round as you like. Both on us be a bit rough but us knows ow to treat a ooman specially when she's a refined ooman like you be. There's plenty of good grub if you likes to cook it, and a fire alf way up the chimney if you likes to tend it an that ud be a welcome state of affairs when us comes in arter our days work instead on a cold grate an a cold pot as us do now. Someever you must please yerself; I bent a gooin to pester you, that I bent."

'Of course you may be thinking I was letting meself down a bit, for as you know I was used to more refined company, but there it was – I wanted a home and he offered one, and in all kindness too, for no kinder heart ever beat than old Sam's, although he was a rough-hewn jewel. So I come. It wasn't long you may be sure before all the neighbours were a gossiping full tilt and so to settle them we decided on matrimony. I liked them both and they liked me, but in the end I chose young Sam. I soon fell into their ways even into their manner of speech – although I was taught at a young ladies' seminary and know my grammar as well as most.

'Ah well, we have to do as Rome does to a certain extent when we live in Rome and that applies to other places too. But (looking at the clock) I shall have to be on the trot for I must make a pudding for the children's supper so must get it on straight away – if you'll excuse me.'

So the visitor took her leave in a somewhat happier mood than when she had come, assured once again by her confidant and friend that there was sure to be a satisfactory solution to the present problem.

And so it was – Harman had been dismissed from his post at the brewery some time before and coming upon someone whom he had known in former days to be an easy prey to duplicity, he had tried to make a little dishonest revenue for himself.

Times are changing

The century was fading out like an old person whose usefulness to others is over and so is no longer of any account. All the world was agog with expectation of great things, in fact a complete change in the plan of existence was looked for in the brave new century ahead. Already the clever ones were deriding the Victorian era with all its narrowness and repressions. What had been mistaken for goodness and stability, they declared now, had only been humbug and hypocrisy in disguise. Now in some mysterious way people were to find themselves upon a different plane altogether, living a fuller and richer life. Soon there would be a king on the throne – the little old queen could not last much longer, the diamond jubilee had been her swan song. A king overflowing with health and good spirits would make a deal of difference to the country and save it from falling altogether into decadence. Gaiety and glamour was to be the order of the day. How all these changes were to come about was not made quite clear. Youth was kicking up its heels higher than ever before – so the elders said, but hadn't they always been saying so – and still are.

The Boer war, which had seemed so impossible to the company of the Fox and Hounds a year ago, was in full swing, but except that it furnished a rich topic of conversation, it made little or no difference to this small community. The young soldier who had helped to enliven that evening a year ago had been sent with his regiment to India before it began and was safely out of it all – to his mother's joy and his own lasting regret for, as he declared in his letters home, his greatest longing was to have a slosh at old Kruger's whiskers.

Robert, who took the *Daily Mail* and read it religiously, was a gold mine of information and on his way home he was always waylaid by Sam who thirsted for news.

'What! Ent old Buller crossed the Tuggler yet?' he would call in an exasperated voice.

'No, not he,' Robert would reply heatedly. 'And it's my opinion that he never will. The Tugla is only a bit of a river. I'd Tugla him if I had my way, I'd go out there and throw him in it.' Apparently they were not at all satisfied with General Buller's management.

'What about that gret gun us a got now? That ought to frit some a them old Boers out o their lurkin places, that it ought.'

'Long Tom you mean. I hear we've got a bigger one out now. I don't think they ought to use such deadly weapons on a lot of poor old farmers, for that's what the Boers are after all.' Robert always had a leaning towards the unpopular party in any dispute.

Old Kruger and his satellites were hated wholeheartedly by practically all the villagers and hamleteers including the children who were given hideous pictures of them on tin brooches, and little round puzzle boxes in which all their teeth, represented by white beads, were rolling loose, and the almost unsolvable puzzle was to get them into a neat row in the pictured enemy's mouth.

The new khaki uniform was another matter for wonderment. How could a soldier shorn of his red coat be a soldier any more? But being an excessively practical race they soon saw the utilitarian side of the change and were all for it.

In compliment to those who wore it the new colour was adopted for everything possible, ugly as it was, blouses, shirts, collars, stationery, crockery and a hundred other items of everyday use wore this unbecoming shade. Eileen's mother treasured some notepaper all her life across which is printed 'This paper is made from the clippings of khaki cloth which made the uniforms our dear soldiers are wearing'.

In the village and hamlet things had been changing rapidly. The gay young parson whom his parishioners had so much enjoyed criticising had gone to a more lucrative 'living in the Midlands', and his place had been taken at first by a middle-aged batchelor who was an ardent collector of antiques and seemed to be perfectly oblivious of his flock unless it happened that on his first – and last – duty call at their cottages he discovered that they were possessed of some piece of china, a chair or table which he coveted; then he persevered, as collectors do, until it became his. He must have been, apart from his stipend, quite a rich man and stories got about of fabulous prices he was willing to pay for odds and ends which were only regarded as rubbish by families to whom they had been handed down. Boxes and outhouses were turned out in hopes of coming across a forgotten pewter plate or candlestick, or perhaps that old pair of china dogs Grannie had brought when she came to live, and they had not thought worthy of the mantel shelf amongst their modern hideosities. When discovered, these found their way to the Rectory with that old chair of Gramp's, which they had been using to saw wood on in the wood shed, as well as the old coffin stool Mother had been using for standing her washing tray on outside. They laughed between themselves at the Rector's liking for such old fashioned things when nice new highly varnished chairs and tables, not to mention the pretty bits of china, could be bought at a price much less than he gave for the old. However they got quite sophisticated about antiques, so much so that the value of them soared and soared in their opinion, until any small piece they had left after this invasion became almost priceless.

Meanwhile the only complaint against this man was that he gave them no cause for complaint – which was rather dull for them, so that they sometimes sighed audibly for the good old days of the arch enemy who at least added a spice of life with his goings on.

But suddenly their dull Rector leapt into the limelight in a breach of promise case with a very young woman living in his previous parish.

This caused terrific excitement; they felt themselves to be injured innocents not to have known all this that was going on under their very noses. A wolf in sheep's clothing, that's what he was, and they didn't need much persuasion from a ringleader to get them to put their names to a 'round robin' praying the Bishop to remove him from their midst; whether it ever reached the Bishop or what was the outcome is not recorded but very soon after this upheaval he went away, having stripped the neighbourhood of its few relics of the past.

Now there would be another new Rector. What would he be like? They wondered and began to feel that it was like putting a hand into the proverbial bag of eels in which one scorpion is concealed – the scorpion was almost sure to be drawn, although there were so many chances against it. But they had a pleasant surprise, the new Rector was a man after their own hearts.

Once again the women were trudging down the muddy field path to 'Mother's Meetings' at the Rectory.

'It doo seem a bit of a treat to goo down ere of a Tuesday – takes anybody out of umselves that it doo,' quoth Mrs Dan'll as she wiped the mud off her boots on the grass verge. 'And Mrs Stretton's just like one of ourselves.'

'Yes, that's just what I likes about er,' replied her crony. 'Don't make you feel you ought to try to talk fine, you can say anything to er just as you think it.'

'Yes that's it. I said to er tother week, "If this ent a lovely cup-o-tay Mrs Stretton I doon't know what is, it tastes no end better than what I makes at home – though I puts plenty in the pot that I do." "Ah-h," she said, "it's just the same when I come to see some of you and you offer me a cup of yours; it tastes much better than my own does. I think it must be something in ourselves and not in the tea – a little change does us the world of good, and when we mothers get together we've so much in common with each other to tell about, it cheers us up to hear each other's views. I do hope it will never be too wet or too snowy for you all to come – I think I should almost cry with disappointment."'

'Yes I truly believe she enjoys herself as much as us do. Its almost like olden times we old Parson about and Miss Grace holdin Mother's Meeting – though o-course she didn't understand us mothers' perdiciments like Mrs Stretton do, see she's had young uns of her own to bring up and knows full well how tantalising they be.'

'Poor old Miss Grace was all very well in her way – as kind as kind if anybody got in a corner like, but she was all for us being down here and the gentry being up there, now there ent none of that we Dr and Mrs Stretton: us be all on a level we them.'

'And what plazes us plazes them. You udn't think Doctor we all his scholarliness ud take any interest in our bits of concerns.'

But he did, for like the Master whom he served, he had the gift of simplicity amounting to greatness. There was nothing that touched the lives of those around him that he held insignificant. Both he and his wife not only taught but practised Socialism in its truest sense.

The two women plodded on talking of the quick and the dead until a shout made them turn round and there was Mrs Rush hurrying along to catch them up.

'Us were just talking about Doctor and Mrs Stretton,' explained Mrs Dan'll, 'and saying how different things be we them in the place.'

'Just what our Joe were saying last night. "'Pon my soul," he sais, "if they doon't fit the place like a pair of old boots that they do."'

But Mrs Rush had lately been on a visit to her married daughter in London, a hitherto unheard of thing to happen to any middle-aged woman of their little community, and it was almost as if the millennium had arrived when she set out, so now the conversation must needs turn to that.

'Town folk be all alike – just like buttons on a card, you can't tell tother from which,' opined Mrs Rich. 'I can't think of none of us who be anything like anybody else, can you?'

'That I can't,' replied Mrs Dan'll's crony, 'weout it be old Emma Moore and Liza Bacon – both on em squints, and I can't abear narn on em.' It was a strange thing that these two elderly women who were quite inoffensive were disliked by most of the others for no other reason than their squint which gave them an air of inquisitiveness – no doubt they were shortsighted, and a pair of spectacles would not only have put their eyes right, but have given their neighbours a new slant on their characters. In fact they were quite different to each other, one a quiet self-effacing woman while the other had a strong inclination to aggressiveness. The three women began to enumerate the people they knew and how little they were alike.

'There's you and me,' began Mrs Rush laughing. 'Nobody could accuse us of being like peas in a pod, now could em?'

'No,' laughed Mrs Dan'll, 'that em couldn't, there's me as big as the side of a house, Bell here no bigger nor our cat sat up beggin, and you that thin anybody can see the wind through you.'

They were still laughing at this when they came to the Rectory gate and passed under the quince tree to the side door. The door opened into the pleasant sitting room which was now set aside for parishioners and where all and sundry found a welcome. They were the first to arrive and they found the Rector and his wife sitting on either side of the glowing fire that had been built to welcome the expected guests. Other women arrived on their heels and the Rector having had a word or two with each of them took himself off to his study, leaving them to their own devices. Mrs Stretton had some news which set them all agog – her only daughter had decided the date of her wedding, the banns were to be called on Sunday, so all the arrangements were discussed and a collective present thought of. They spoke of the flowers they would bring to help decorate the church for the ceremony, for by then the spring flowers would be out and they could send the children to the wood to gather white violets.

Of course Mrs Rush's visit to London was discussed and more about the queer folk that lived there, and the things she had seen – Madam Tussaud's had been wonderful though she couldn't help laughing at herself for being taken in by that policeman.

'I don't see why we shouldn't all go for a day this coming summer,' said Mrs Stretton. 'It wouldn't cost a lot. We must begin saving up at once. We could visit Madam Tussaud's, then have a nice lunch, see a few of the large shops in Oxford Street, then perhaps you would like to go to some other place of interest before we had tea and made for home. We mustn't attempt too much or it will be too tiring for the older ones. What do you say to it?'

This was flabbergasting. For a moment they were speechless – then their tongues fell over each other. Of course it was only a wild dream for the present, but eventually it did materialise – and from that day sophistication of the parish has never paused.

Epilogue

'Oh Mother! What can I do now?' cried a little girl towards the ending of a long long summer day. The harvest holidays had seemed endless and despite her inborn resourcefulness she could find no further inspiration within herself, having exhausted all known occupations and amusements. The mother, who to the child was a bottomless mine of wisdom, thought intently for a moment, then said brightly, 'Why not make yourself a pin-a-sight, my child? By the way I'm short of pins and a few would come in useful.'

The child, to whom the combination of business and pleasure appealed strongly, ran off joyfully to collect the necessary materials, her slight boredom gone like snow before a sunbeam. From amongst her treasures she produced a small square of glass, a larger square of paper, and from the garden a handful of carefully chosen flower petals. The glass was placed in the centre of the paper, the petals arranged on the glass with a row of white ones across the top. The paper was then carefully folded parcelwise over them, and some white cotton from the family workbasket made the parcel secure. This was then turned over and a little shutter made by cutting three sides of a square in the paper, the upper side acting as a hinge. A lovely little kaleidoscope of colour was thus revealed. The child ran off elated, and when she came upon two of her friends, she brought it out proudly from behind her back as she chanted, 'A pin to see a pin-a-sight, all the ladies dressed in white standing up in the turnpike. But I must have a pin before you see it.' After much searching one was produced, the curtain raised, and the show within admired to the full by the little girls who joyfully accompanied the little show woman on her journey round the hamlet. The show was exhibited to all they met, pin or no pin, but always rewarded by an admiring glance.

So no matter if you are pin rich or not, you are welcome to peep beneath the curtain that time has woven at this little community, who